The Space Between

Breast cancer & finding me

Jacqui Taylor

Dedication

To Paul, Nathaniel and Robin - emerging from the dark was about finding you all there on the other side.

For all the cancer rebels who have gone before me or are yet to come. Let us inspire each other to be courageous, to face the challenge head-on and commit to living this life.

Contents

Foreword

We all know about breast cancer, the importance of regularly checking your breasts and the pink ribbon. That is probably where most of us stop in our knowledge. Until we are diagnosed with breast cancer or someone we love is diagnosed. Then everything changes.

That's when we suddenly realise how little we know and how desperately we look for information to make sense of it all, to not feel so lonely, to manage the all-encompassing fear that sits alongside a cancer diagnosis.

The Space Between is a powerful, personal and informative memoir of how Jacqui navigated this journey of moving from not knowing to knowing and the space between.

It is not just knowing about breast cancer and understanding the diagnosis and the treatments, the side effects and the results, it is getting to know yourself in a new and deep way.

"Chemotherapy treatment strips you back to the bare bones. Unreservedly, it forces you to see who you are. In doing so, I found a place to take so much care of myself that I love me and cherish my body. By listening and paying attention, I am guided to what I need."

Often when we think about cancer, we think about survival. Jacqui shows us that in what might start as a fight for survival, there is a deep opportunity for change and in that way we might be more alive than ever – in this moment of irreversible change. And it is also in this space that we begin to understand that we are also stronger than we ever thought.

Her unbelievable tenacity and strength shines through the book and underlines her attitude towards the diagnosis.

"Accept it, Jacqui. Get on with changing it."

She says she quickly learned many new skills – new ways of living, finding her flow in ways she never thought possible. Her cancer journey confronts her with the reality that even in moments like this, you have choices. To make your own choices is a right that can give you strength in situations like this and by sharing her story, she encourages the reader to not forfeit that right and give the choice to others.

Her story is one of deep bravery and courage – a strength of heart – that shows us tangibly what radical acceptance looks like. It is not about giving up, it is about accepting what IS. Right here. In this moment.

Jacqui shares her struggle of wanting to find someone to blame, she vividly describes the fury and anger that is so hard to sit with and she describes how at the other side of blame is peace. Feeling all the feelings is one of the profound messages that emerges from Jacqui's story. At times it seems impossible, and yet, to allow feelings as they are and move through them becomes the hallmark of the space between.

The fact that Jacqui navigated cancer during COVID meant that she was on her own when she received the diagnosis and many other moments that made her experience especially challenging. The way Jacqui describes her experience moves you to tears, it is as if you are standing by her side, experiencing the many acts of kindness from strangers, like when someone touches her shoulder with the bare hand, no glove, as she is undergoing a torturous procedure, to let her know she is not alone.

Perhaps the greatest achievement of *The Space Between* is that Jacqui is radically honest and authentic, at no point trying to embellish any parts of her story. One moment you are reading and you marvel at her strength and then the next moment you are there with her as she breaks and your heart breaks and then you know THAT is the real strength, to allow yourself to break. Thank you, Jacqui, for sharing the space between with us.

Brita Fernandez Schmidt, Author of *Fears to Fierce – A Woman's Guide to Owning Her Power* and Transformational Coach.

"*And once the storm is over, you won't remember how you made it through, how you managed to survive. You won't even be sure whether the storm is really over. But one thing is certain. When you come out of the storm, you won't be the same person who walked in. That's what this storm's all about.*"

— *Haruki Murakami, Kafka on the Shore*

Prologue

Someone pulls the emergency stop cord on the train. About to take a sip of my coffee, I am caught unawares and the whole mouthful spills over my shirt. I drop the rest of the cup in surprise and the hot liquid soaks through to my skin, all over the table and my trousers.

As the train's brakes kick in and we grind to a halt, my bag falls off the overhead shelf and all my belongings scatter into the carriage aisle. Why hadn't I closed it properly? Everyone must be looking at me now. I feel so embarrassed. Yet, as I look around, most of the carriage are quietly minding their own business, oblivious to my distress. One kind woman sitting opposite me hands over a tissue to wipe off the coffee and the man across the aisle picks up my purse and places it on the table. I stand up, but as I don't know what to do first to rectify the situation, I look around the rest of the carriage pretending something will come to mind. I peer out of the window, trying to work out where we are and how far I have left to go. The fields outside tell me nothing. I am somewhere I do not recognise. A place I must have sped past before. I won't be sitting back down there; the seat is covered in the remains of my spilt drink. I have no idea what to do, so I wait for the guard's announcement, staring blankly out of the window. Stationary. Still. Despite the uncertainty, I am slowly beginning to make more sense of the scenery beyond the window. Ah, so this is where I am. Without a seat in this carriage, I'd better collect my belongings and look elsewhere. The train starts to move once more.

Before leaving, I glance around at the familiar faces of the people I travelled with. Many look somewhat weary and tired. It's been a long journey, and they all have places to be, so they could do without any further delays. A raise of a head to acknowledge my departure with a slightly uncomfortable smile, unsure whether they should say something. Another wishes me a quiet "good luck".

As the train pulls away, I gather up my things and try to decide what to do with them. Do I even still want them? Other passengers return to their conversations, their books, or their devices, no longer interested in the reason for the stop. Unsure where I will find another seat, I make my way through to the next carriage clutching the half-empty bag to my chest. I pause momentarily in the space between, where the sound of the train moving over the tracks fills my awareness. Wait here. Catch your breath. Calm down a little and stop worrying about the coffee stains on your clothes. No one cares. With a deep breath, I walk towards the next carriage. Immediately, heads turn to see who has caused the doors to slide open. They smile at me; one says "hello", another moves her bag so I can sit down at their table. With an awkward grin, I place my bag beneath my feet and settle into the conversation. I feel my breath slow down, my heart follows, some of the tension leaves my shoulders and jaw. I even laugh at a joke. I relax back into my seat with the knowledge I'll be alright here.

We're moving along at speed now. I feel less awkward as we've spent the time chatting and swapping anecdotes since the train set off. Yes, I am going to be alright here I repeat in my head. I can sit back and try to make the most of the journey. Outside the window the countryside sweeps past my eyes. From the window seat, I rest my head back against the chair and withdraw from the chatter to capture a quiet moment for myself. There is still a long way to go. There will be plenty of time to re-join the conversation. Will this tunnel never end? Through the glass, all I can see is my reflection staring back at me from the darkness. The green fields and blue sky that held me in a trance for a few miles are interrupted by the blackness. As the sound of the train on the track rattles in my ears, my eyes fill with unexpected tears which then delicately trickle down my cheeks. Unsettled and embarrassed to look back at my companions, I choose to remain absorbed by my own image. What is happening? Stay calm. It will all be fine once you get there. You'll work something out.

"Heard you were here." My head spins towards the familiar voice and is met by the warm smile of an old friend. "Thought it was you. Are you alright?" Buoyed by her presence, the sadness gradually lifts and we ease into a discussion. She knows me. I have confidence she'll have a good suggestion.

My friend wishes me well before she makes her way back to the doors of the next carriage. Her arrival was an unanticipated but much-welcomed surprise. Our brief conversation even more so. "I'm only in the next coach if you need me," I am reminded.

I laugh as one of my new companions finishes her tale and notice how easy it feels to be with these strangers who know so little about me. Enjoying each other's company without the need to place them anywhere. I listen and share in return. I forget that we appear to be in the same tunnel. I'm not even sure where we are going anymore. There has been no station for a while. Nothing I can do right now about it. Tired of looking at my reflection in the window I remain engaged in our conversation. That feels better.

Thoughts pass through my mind about what has happened that

day and what is to come. It certainly is not the best day I've ever had, sitting here in coffee-stained clothes, missing half my stuff and running late for the engagement at my end-destination. It is what it is. I will work it out. It was perfectly reasonable to be flustered but now I must keep a calm head, breathe and get through the rest of the day, step by step. I'll be on my own once I depart the train, as enjoyable as it is to pass the time listening to new voices. I can cope.

Suddenly there is a disturbance "Excuse us please, can we get through? Oh, there you are. We've been looking for you. Here is a drink and a sandwich. Do you need anything else?" I look up to see two of my fellow commuters from the other carriage cheerfully bustling through. It is terrific to see them; we've shared many a journey along the way. I feel safe, and I remember how well they know me, no explanation required. All those conversations shared over the years as our lives intersected on this route. Thoughtful and considerate, always there when I need them. Polite introductions follow before another passenger asks if they might keep going along the aisle. "See you soon. You know where we are."

Wow! This feels like a long journey. Leaving the station this morning seems like an age ago. My mood has settled, like a pebble on a beach, gently rolling with the tide, in and out, but content to be where it ends up. I rub my eyes to adjust to the light, bringing more awareness to my surroundings after my short nap. Finally! We've reached the end of that dark tunnel and the new landscape reveals itself. The carriage has more of a buzz about it; we must be approaching a stop because people are collecting their luggage off the racks. The seats around me are occupied by new faces. I must have missed others leaving the train while I slept. This isn't my stop, though. A little bit further to go.

I peer out of the window. Nearly there. I wonder if I should get up now, collect my bags, and wait closer to the door. A fellow passenger at my table gestures toward me and says, "What's the rush? There will be plenty of time once the guard announces the upcoming destination. Enjoy the last part of the journey. You'll have enough to think about when you get off. Make the most of these last few minutes." I shrug my shoulders in agreement and settle back. No panic. Remember to find the space. All the other stuff is going to happen regardless. Just 'be' for a while longer.

I'm here. My destination. Time to collect what is left of my belongings and leave the train. I say my goodbyes to those I have shared the journey with, expressing a desire to meet again. I thank them for their support and openness for giving a seat to what must have seemed like a slightly crazy woman covered in coffee stains clutching her possessions. I express my gratitude that they made light of it and made me feel so welcome and comfortable. I look around to see if anyone I know is still in the other carriage, but it is busier there now and I cannot recognise anyone. No time to linger. I make my way hurriedly down the train steps. Just like that, I am on the platform. As abruptly as the train halted earlier on, my journey is over. Standing alone, in the fresh air feeling exposed and unsure.

Where am I? The surroundings feel strangely obscure, yet it is the right place. Something has changed from a previous visit. I pause to recall what I had decided to do to rectify the day. Too late for my appointment, I need to explore an alternative way to spend my time. Right, I know what I will do. I take one last look at the train disappearing down the track before I turn to the exit of the station. I'm quite excited to see what's going to be outside the door. This feels like unknown territory for me, but I need to explore this place. Maybe not for long, but this is where I am now. Let's see what there is to find and enjoy the experience.

1

Emergency Stop

"We cannot change the cards we are dealt, just how we play the game."

— *Randy Pausch, American Educator, Professor at Carnegie Mellon University, Pittsburgh*

"I'm afraid you have breast cancer." The surgeon looked over the top of her blue mask, trying to deliver the news with sincerity and compassion in half a face. In those COVID times, I was alone. My husband was waiting in the car outside, unaware that our lives had changed forever. Tuesday 28th July 2020.

I can picture the surgeon sitting in front of me against the slightly pallid orange walls, the two nurses standing off to one side, one by the small sink, the other by one of the doors, and I can feel them all watching me, waiting for a reaction. In that moment, the world stopped as my mind tried to process the words.

My heart did not race. My face did not flush. I did not panic. A calm numbness enveloped me and muffled all the sounds from the outside world. Everyone else in the room faded out of focus, yet I felt all eyes on me, and I had absolutely no idea what I was supposed to do next.

I had spent the afternoon in the breast clinic moving from room to room and test to test. In between, I sat in the waiting area with some books, trying to do some work. I was one day into a five-day online marketing course and had brought my homework with me to do in preparation for the evening session when I returned home. There I was, carrying on as if nothing was happening - getting on with things, making progress - so Jacqui!

After the surgeon's initial examination, I had a sense that all was not well.

"Yes, that side feels a bit lumpier and there is the puckering of the skin. Let's get the scans done and see what they find."

I started with a mammogram, which, if you have never had one, is one of the most horrid, degrading procedures. So I was simply glad when that was over. Next stop was an ultrasound. Whilst probably not as busy as usual due to COVID, the clinic had a steady flow of women moving from room to room with their baskets containing their clothes (as we all wore those unflattering green or blue hospital gowns). Everyone was on their own, sitting safely apart to comply with the social distancing rules - red and white tape across every other seat. No one really spoke. What would you say? We all knew why we were there, and you could hardly strike up a conversation through a mask across the room.

They had clearly found something on the ultrasound scan, but I quietly accepted it as I lay there in the dark room, my right arm above my head, propped up on my left side. While the radiologist took the breast tissue and lymph node biopsies, I chatted with the radiographer about how it had been for them working during the initial lockdown; like it was a routine check-up.

As I lay there, it reminded me of when my eldest son was delivered by elective caesarean section, and throughout the delivery, I talked with the anaesthetist about our last skiing holiday. During my physiotherapy training, I had been in theatre and observed a delivery via caesarean section, so that image was in the front of my mind. Believe me, it is not something you want to visualise when it is happening to you. I do not know to this day whether the delivery team thought I was the weirdest expectant mum they had ever had on the table as I showed no apparent interest in the 'birth' - which, of course, is not true. My wish was that the birth of my firstborn was not overridden by the images of someone else's delivery! Distraction or denial? Either way it enabled me to keep my composure.

I was told I would need to wait a week for the results of the biopsy but that the surgeon would speak to me about my next appointment before I left. When they called me back in and the surgeon plus two other nurses entered the consulting room, I knew it was not good news. In no situation did it take three people to give me an appointment time.

'Is there someone here with you?' the surgeon asked.

How could I make that call to Paul, my husband, knowing he would immediately realise it was bad news? That moment of looking in his eyes as the surgeon repeated the diagnosis brought waves of nausea over me, and the tears followed.

That word we all dread. That moment you pray will not happen to you. I had no reason to think I would get cancer. There is no family history of it, so it never figured on the list of health issues I was concerned about. How wrong I was.

When I initially noticed the change in the appearance of my right breast sometime during the first UK COVID lockdown in spring

2020, cancer was not the first thing that came to my mind, and I did not concern myself with it. There was too much else going on as my physiotherapy business was haemorrhaging money; I went from a full appointment book to an empty one overnight on the 23rd of March 2020 after the prime minister announced the first lockdown. I worked tirelessly to save my business, pivot to a new mode of working and spent my time on endless Zoom calls in business groups with other people in the same boat as me. I can honestly say I gave little thought to the weird way the bottom of my right breast seemed to disappear when I lifted my right arm overhead. I mentioned it in passing one day to Paul, who didn't think it was anything sinister. I kept looking and wondering what it might be. Then I went back to 'work' mode.

On reflection, it could not have been anything else. From my professional life, I knew that my breast would not have looked that way if it was something insignificant. As the breast tissue was puckered and drawn inwards - 'hugging the lesion' as Jean-Pierre Barral, the French Osteopath, would say - the tumour was drawing the skin in, making itself known to my conscious self. My body had been aware of it for a long time but simply had not chosen to tell me yet. It must have been there, gradually becoming more obvious, but I hadn't seen it. How did I miss it?

It was not until a bike ride with a friend, Gaenor, in July during those brief but lovely few weeks when some of the restrictions were lifted, that I really discussed it with anyone. She, of course, said I needed to see a doctor, and sure enough, I phoned up on Monday morning to make an appointment. The GP saw me in person that very afternoon, and the referral was made for the breast clinic for the following Tuesday.

That week I was in a daze, going through the motions at work. I told my reception team and a few close friends what was happening. People did that thing where they naturally want to offer you support but with a positive spin. "I'm sure it'll be nothing." "It will be fine, but best to get it checked out." I nodded back in agreement to contain any deeper emotions or worries that might bubble up to the surface if I really started to think about what was going on.

I was busy in the clinic - my diary had been full since we reopened to see people in person back in June. I'd been knocking out 12-plus-hour days with all the extra procedures and cleaning that was required. It had been fabulous to get clients back in after weeks of only seeing them online, but many naturally carried a higher level of anxiety than before. We all had our collective experience of the lockdown, which weaved itself through the treatment sessions. The level of my emotional labour was higher than normal. I was exhausted, but there was a light at the end of the tunnel, albeit quite a small one.

I felt an element of finality as the week progressed, and by Friday, a real sense of what was happening to me became apparent. I wasn't due to be at work until the following Thursday for various reasons, so I had some much-needed breathing space before my appointment on Tuesday. As I walked home that Friday evening, I said to myself, "If I've got cancer, I am never working this fucking hard again."

We left the clinic with a bagful of leaflets and an appointment to see the surgeon the following Wednesday for the biopsy results. At the time, I believe I felt calm, but on reflection, I was stunned; staring out at the rest of the world as I moved through the waiting area, the hospital corridors and back to our car. What was there to say? It is possible that I made some nervous, mindless conversation to fill the awkward silence. Honestly, I am not sure. I know that once I was back in the car, I saw the messages on my phone from a couple of friends waiting to hear back from me. I called Liz first as she was the one I'd talked to most about the upcoming appointment. Liz worked with me and over the years has become one of my dearest friends. I knew I could tell her first. I almost did not need to say anything when she picked up the phone. A pause, a brief silence before I said, "It's bad news, I'm afraid", and that was enough for her to realise. Why is it that you feel worse telling others when it is your life that has been turned on its head?

The one person I had not talked to about the clinic visit was my youngest son, Matthew. There seemed no point in worrying him if it was all nothing. I truly had no sense of how he might react. As it turned out, I should have known that my gentle, intelligent child would take it in his stride. Paul told him initially, and then he came into our sitting room and gave me the biggest hug. He said nothing, but then it was unnecessary. His brother, Nathaniel, was not home that evening, so we telephoned. In typical teenage fashion, he had forgotten about my appointment that day, but he took the news extremely well. His resilience shining through as ever. I was almost pleased that he was with friends so he could process the information in his own time.

'*Stationary. Still.*' I sat on our sofa, staring out the bay window at the leaves moving on the trees outside. This gave me something to focus on as I made those calls - my best friends, mother-in-law, sister. My sense of calmness was probably more accurately described as the numbness of emotional shock. I was a witness to my actions and words, but nothing seemed to settle within me. There weren't tears and hours of recriminations that evening. Once I was finished with phone calls, we settled down to a quiet evening - I didn't look at my phone, I didn't Google anything. As the surgeon suggested, it was better to wait until we had the full picture before I disappeared down any rabbit holes online.

That day I entered Cancer Land. A place I did not realise existed until I am shown the secret door. Like Lucy finding her way through the coats in the wardrobe to enter Narnia. I know I have stepped into a different world that I know virtually nothing about. I have no idea what I will find there as I take those first few steps forward. I certainly know that there is no stepping back inside the wardrobe and pretending I never saw the lamppost or the snow. I know my life has changed forever. Like Lucy, there are people I want with me as I tackle the expedition. As Lucy found Mr Tumnus and made new friends and had new experiences that she could not share with Susan, Peter and Edmund, I too started to make new acquaintances. Strangers to me but days before, these women suddenly have so much more in common with me than my best friends, whom I have known for over 30 years.

On that day, I knew none of this. I did not know all the possibilities that would unfold - only that I was in a different place. What we did not know was the extent of the diagnosis. How severe was the cancer? Has it spread elsewhere? The biopsy results the following week would give us more insight; in the meantime, we had to play the waiting game. We were due to go away for a few days the following week to the Lake District, just the two of us, for a much-needed break after the craziness of COVID and the lockdown. The surgeon, Ms Cathy Tait, recommended we still go and return for the clinic appointment the following Wednesday.

Ever pragmatic, I went into full Jacqui 'organising and planning' mode the following day. However stunned I was by the news, I knew I would not be able to rest until I had sorted out a few things. What would happen with work? For a few hours, I vaguely entertained the idea of going to work that Thursday and Friday to see my full client list. Then I thought, *how can I? How can I remotely give the service that I expect of myself to people when my mind is elsewhere?* I couldn't take someone's money to be 100% distracted by my pending results. Decision made - clear the decks. I'm not coming in.

How would we manage all my client bookings? How would we tell people? One thing I knew from the start was that I wanted to be upfront, honest and open with people. I saw no value in making this the elephant in the room. There was no point in keeping it a secret. Why would I? Yes, our health issues are personal, but my whole life was turned on its head. How could I live without all those I encounter being aware of what was happening?

There was also a completely selfish motive here too. I needed to tell people. I needed to say those words out loud – "I have been diagnosed with breast cancer". A way to make it real and solidified in my head, my very being, was to repeat those words. I was compelled to share how I felt. Perhaps more than that, I could explore how I felt, and with every conversation, I could delve deeper within myself to understand and identify my emotions. From somewhere deep inside, there was an inner resolve, a composure. Life happens to us. It is not a static state. There are many phases to it, each a different game with different rules. If right at that moment it felt like the odds were stacked against me, then I was not going to crumble. Game of chance or not. This is the hand I had been dealt. Now I had to play it.

Our mini-break to the Lakes was absolutely what we needed. We had booked to stay at the most gorgeous B&B outside of Keswick, and it was perfect. The couple who ran it were so welcoming, and even in our shellshocked state, we somehow relaxed and switched off. The weather was lousy, despite being August - typical Lake District - but we made the best of it. The hostess, Sheena, was a welcome distraction, as one morning, we sat in front of the fire and chatted about their new B&B venture, her kids and, of course, the lockdown and COVID. I felt no need to share my life-changing news with her. I wanted to have these two days to keep it at arm's length.

We did not avoid the subject particularly, but we also did not have any conversations that might lead us down the dark alleys of where this diagnosis might take us. I had a few moments of tears. There was a gorgeous roll-top bath in our room, so I took full advantage. I soaked in the hot water and bubbles up to my neck as I allowed my mind to drift aimlessly but go nowhere.

I was in this space between what I was before and what I would become. Not thinking too far ahead as to what might be. Not consciously. There was a knowing deep within that this was not what I needed. This was the start of experiencing being in the present moment. Sitting in that front room with Sheena, listening to her stories. Allowing myself to be absorbed in her words and not dwelling on what might be lurking in my mind. For someone who is quite open and happy to share, it was interesting that I chose not to. Maybe all the phone calls over the previous days had satisfied that need in me. This time was for something else.

We needed to leave early for the clinic appointment on Wednesday morning, so we said our goodbyes and got on the road. The pathology results confirmed that I had Grade 2 Invasive Lobular Breast Cancer, but the lymph node biopsy was clear, suggesting it was contained within the right breast. That was a relief. At that point, it appeared surgery would be the primary treatment. Lobular Breast Cancer, whilst the second most common type of breast cancer, only accounts for 10-15% of cases and presents differently to the most common form, Ductal Breast Cancer. Over the coming weeks, I was going to become far more knowledgeable about all of this.

Strangely, we were both relieved that day, as it seemed I had got away with the best possible results. Paul shared with me that he had been dreading it was more advanced, and his mood lightened. In Cancer Land, I have learnt that you must take every positive win, no matter how small, and sit with it and acknowledge it is a good result. However insignificant it may appear, recognising when something bad does not happen gives you a psychological boost that is so needed in this place. I had breast cancer. My life was now on a different path than the week before.

———————

'Someone pulls the emergency stop cord on the train. About to take a sip of my coffee, I am caught unawares and the whole mouthful spills over my shirt. I drop the rest of the cup in surprise and the hot liquid soaks through to my skin, all over the table and my trousers.

As the train's brakes kick in and we grind to a halt, my bag falls off the overhead shelf and all my belongings scatter into the carriage aisle. Why hadn't I closed it properly? Everyone must be looking at me now. I feel so embarrassed. Yet, as I look around, most of the carriage are quietly minding their own business, oblivious to my distress. One kind woman sitting opposite me hands over a tissue to wipe off the coffee and the man across the aisle picks up my purse and places it on the table. I stand up, but as I don't know what to do first to rectify the situation, I look around the rest of the carriage pretending something will come to mind. I peer out of the window, trying to work out where we are and how far I have left to go. The fields outside tell me nothing. I am somewhere I do not recognise. A place I must have sped past before. I won't be sitting back down there; the seat is covered in the remains of my spilt drink. I have no idea what to do, so I wait for the guard's announcement, staring blankly out of the window. Stationary. Still.

Despite the uncertainty, I am slowly beginning to make more sense of the scenery beyond the window. Ah, so this is where I am. Without a seat in this carriage, I'd better collect my belongings and look elsewhere. The train starts to move once more.'

———————

2

Acceptance

"Life is a series of natural and spontaneous changes. Don't resist them; that only creates sorrow. Let reality be reality. Let things flow naturally forward in whatever way they like."

— *Lao Tzu, Chinese Philosopher*

How do you take in the enormity of finding out that you have cancer? I'm not sure you do immediately. Whilst I did cope well and could function, I accept now that I was in shock. The full extent of what having cancer means takes considerable time to absorb, and that meaning evolves as you move through the experience. That said, during those early days I adapted quickly to the news, almost with a voice in my head saying, "I told you so". Somewhere within me, I knew I was pushing myself to the edge. Nevertheless, a cancer diagnosis was entirely unexpected.

To reach a state of acceptance near the beginning of my journey contributed significantly to making sense of it all in those early days. There was a brief moment as I first got in the car after receiving the diagnosis when I felt all the rage and anguish of the previous few months take over me. Not only the cancer diagnosis but the stress of COVID and battling to keep the business afloat engulfed me. I cried angrily, I most probably cursed, and called out a few people and shouted, "it's not fair,'" a couple of times then I stopped. That was the first pause. The first pause of many to follow and those still to arrive. I let all that blame go and let it be for that moment.

It made no difference what people had done or if their actions had somehow contributed to a situation that may have contributed to the stress that may have contributed to the cancer! Whatever the history, it altered nothing in that moment because I was the one who had cancer. Even the most earnest apology was not going to change that.

All I had was where I was at that precise moment in time, what I was going to do and how I was going to respond. Desperately feeling the need to blame other people was not going to serve me well, and I needed to stop. To this day, I am proud of how quickly I was able to curb this train of thought.

That said, I have revisited my crazy blame game when things have hit rock bottom. When I am afraid, absolutely yes, it's easy to strike out and seek someone else to shoulder the burden. But I work hard to prevent these emotions from consuming me. The cold reality is that behaving and responding differently to past circumstances had been within my control. I owe it to myself to take responsibility for that. With no judgement or blame, that was simply how it was. From now on, I would choose to respond, not react, wherever I could.

The natural questions arise as to whether I had not been vigilant enough about checking my breasts. How had I missed it and let myself down so badly? Again, I recall that I hit the pragmatic button early on. Nothing I could feel, say or do at that point would change the facts of the matter. I had Lobular Breast Cancer. FACT. What was done was done. Building up a lot of bitterness about the unfairness of this happening to me was unnecessary. To blame myself for previous poor decisions or choices would only turn into self-loathing and hate. From the outset, I wished to do my utmost to avoid becoming the victim in this story.

As I sit here writing this, I question if I really did hold it together this calmly. Or is this me just making it sound more self-assured for dramatic effect? Anyone who spoke with me during those first few days may recall that I was genuinely composed. I have thought long and hard about this. I did cry, but the floodgates never fully opened. Perhaps it was my version of survival mode where deep down I was preserving my emotional energy for the long road ahead. The emotion found its way out along the journey. At the start, I wanted to hold it together for fear that if I let it slide, I might be unable to bring it back.

In the day or so that followed, as I allowed the reality to settle in my body, I accepted the situation right to my deepest core. A situation I could not change. An event that was happening to me that had no opt-out.

I have one clear memory, which I may well have made up, but as I see it so vividly in my mind's eye, I like to believe that it happened. I'm standing in my garden. It's been a sunny day, and I have been sitting on the patio steps making a couple of phone calls to friends. It's possibly only the next day, maybe two days after the diagnosis. It wasn't very long. I remember feeling this heavy weight in the pit of my stomach. Slightly sickening. I feel like this is it. This is my body, the universe, some higher power, whoever I want to believe in, telling me that enough is enough. Telling me that this time I have to stop and I have to listen. I've ignored time and time again those other physical symptoms that had suggested my body was struggling under the stress. I gave them a cursory glance, maybe altering my diet or making some changes in my life before the less good habits slowly crept back in. I can see the leaves on the beautiful purple Hazel tree that we have in our garden in front of me, adjacent to the white flowers of the buddleia, with all the butterflies in it. That is the image that comes to my mind whenever I think about this conversation with myself - the green leaves and white column of flowers of the buddleia contrast against the purple, leathery leaves of the Hazel. As that feeling of sickness and fear starts to ebb away, a sensation of relief rises through my body like a lightness coming up through my abdomen, into my chest and out to my shoulders, where they soften and widen, my head balancing on the top of my spine with ease. The relief of letting go and acceptance. I only have this to think about. The one thing that is important in the next few weeks and months is that I get better. Whatever else is going on needs to take a backseat. That means the business. That means worrying about other people and what they think.

Whilst experiencing this feeling of relief, a weightlessness came over me. I felt quite happy. I felt like all the worry was gone. There was nothing that needed to be sorted out or dealt with. There was no need for my body to continue to fight with me rather than us working together to get through this. It felt like a second chance. It really felt like I could start again; my expectations changed. This could be an opportunity for me to change my life. I'd held on to so much, too frightened to let go, fearing the uncertainty of what might happen if I did. The uncertainty over my life was now at the forefront of my mind, but not as something I could influence.

Acceptance. I've read so much about this since my diagnosis - how important it is to accept the things we cannot change. This feels almost like one of the few times in my life I came to that realisation so quickly and calmly. My inner strength was there without having to be called upon. It was already there, ready. This is happening - nothing I do is going to change it.

I am so proud of this. This power swelled within me to trust that I could cope, acknowledging it would be hard but I would meet it. Yet in a different way to how I had previously - not by fighting and battling against myself and everyone else.

"I cannot fight everyone and everything. I know I have the strength in me to fight the disease, but I must do it whilst looking after myself." I had to look after myself - my mind and body.

Like a game of Tetris, the final block appeared at the top of my screen to complete the row and it all fell into place. People talk about a deep, inner knowing intuition - this was one of those moments.

The 'old' Jacqui could cope too. She had a different way of calling upon her resilience and mental toughness, though. She armoured up and prepared to take on the world without respite. Whatever the world threw at her, she could find a way through but ignored the wounds she collected along the way.

She hadn't always been that way. There was a time when she did take more care, but the more self-reliant she became and the more she tried to fit into the environment, the less she was able to make sense of it. She always wanted to do her best but forgot she was the measure of that, not the outside world. The need for validation led her down some dark alleys that took her a while to find her way out of.

The immediate run-up to my diagnosis was a distorted time as we lived those first few months of the pandemic. As a small business owner, like so many others my back was up against the wall. We were all doing our best to survive. I know now that I did this at the expense of many of those closest to me, but at the time, I felt like I was drowning. I was reaching out to whoever could offer me a life raft that would save this entity, this living, breathing thing that was my business. I can't change that now, but when I look back, I'm not sure I am very fond of this former Jacqui. She never meant to be unkind, thoughtless or hard on anyone else; she was simply in survival mode.

Over the years of running my business, I had many wonderful experiences and met and worked with some incredible people. I strived to improve and make progress. Ambition was always there. Whereas I attempted to take people along with me, there were occasions when things didn't work out as I had hoped, but I always chose to get back up. I was never easily defeated. The one thing I most definitely was, and still am, is resilient. I could take on whatever the world threw at me and, for the most part, overcome it. Or at least reach an acceptable conclusion. This approach of armouring up to take on the world, brushing myself off, getting back up again and repeating it, whilst admirable, is exhausting. I didn't know another way, though. The control freak in me wanted to have certainty and know what was to come. The high expectations and judgement I placed on myself were extended to those around me. More often than not, none of us lived up to it. I was never truly comfortable with bobbing along on the tide or looking out of the train window and letting the scenery just pass me by. I would be that person on the train with all my books out, on my laptop or phone, doing something and making the most of my time, using my time wisely, rarely seeing it as space to breathe.

'Letting things flow naturally in whatever way they like.'

I picked this quote as I was about to learn an early lesson in going with the flow. My full diagnosis was to take another four weeks to confirm through more tests and more waiting for the results. It was a crash course in learning how to go with the flow.

I was starting to learn more about the specifics of Lobular breast cancer. There is not always a lump as the cancer cells grow in a single-file pattern through the breast tissue. This is because of the absence of a protein known as E-cadherin. Consequently, this growth pattern of single cells and straight lines can make lobular harder to see on imaging, in particular mammograms.

In my case, the mammogram had not shown the tumour - partly because of the diffuse nature of the cancer but also because I have glandular, denser breast tissue. This makes it harder to see the contrast between healthy and abnormal tissue on the scan. The realisation began to dawn on mew that possibly this tumour was present 2 years before when I had my first mammogram as part of the screening programme. Nothing I could do about that now but a chilling thought all the same. Due to this, it is routine for all patients diagnosed with Lobular to have an additional MRI scan to clarify the exact size of the tumour.

Sure enough, the results from the MRI showed a greater area of concern on the right as well as something on the left. I felt that I was moving deeper into the tunnel as my presentation became less straight forward. Further ultrasound biopsies were able to confirm findings for the right, but the team were unable to access the area on the left side via an ultrasound biopsy. I needed an MRI-guided biopsy, which as an aerosol-generating procedure, meant that I had to isolate for two weeks prior. The radiologist who was trained to perform the procedure was not available until the start of September, which seemed so far away. Then the full extent of the impact of COVID kicked in. A specific piece of equipment was unavailable for weeks in the UK, and other hospitals could not help. Despite the best efforts of the medical team, who made their own calls to their local hospital contacts to see if they could source the equipment or carry out the procedure, we got nowhere. I was told I had to wait for the equipment and that the Bradford hospital was top of the list with the Belgium supplier as soon as one became available. The date for the biopsy was set for the 2nd of September, subject to the kit arriving. Tentatively, the surgery date was set for the 14th of September, which gave us time for the results to come back. More waiting.

I was in a tailspin. Why did I have to wait before the tumour in the right was removed? Was there a risk it would spread? We'd been having conversations about implants and how I could have further surgery to balance out the left side and joking at home about fake boobs and whether I would end up swimming in an odd way if I had one boob that was more like a float! The light-heartedness of these conversations became more distant as the seriousness of what was actually going on became increasingly apparent. I set about making phone calls to my private medical insurance to see if I could have the surgery done by them sooner or whether I could change to a different hospital trust. I hated the feeling of my life literally being in someone else's hands. I wanted to get on with it. The calls were fruitless. I was consistently told that a full diagnosis was required before I should have anything done and moving about wasn't going to make that happen any quicker. Acceptance. Go with the flow.

Treading water. Waiting. Helpless. I was rubbish at sitting and waiting, but I was learning. During this time, I began to meet new people, other women who were ahead of me on this journey. Through friends and Facebook groups, I started to have increasingly more conversations. Time and again grateful for these strangers giving so generously of themselves. Sharing their stories with me and listening so caringly to mine. To feel such a bond with another who is otherwise unknown to you is a rare situation created through uncomfortable circumstances. They provided something others could not, through no fault of their own. A narrow gap opened between myself and those I had known for years. This never changed relationships, and my dear friends have been the most incredible support for me through all of this. However, I found myself drawn to seek others' counsel as I negotiated this strange new world.

I still had to start my isolation even though we didn't know if the kit would arrive. Only a few days before the procedure was due to take place, the phone call came from a very happy breast care nurse to tell me that the magic piece of equipment had arrived! The relief was immense.

'Before leaving, I glance around at the familiar faces of the people I travelled with. Many look somewhat weary and tired. It's been a long journey, and they all have places to be, so they could do without any further delays. A raise of a head to acknowledge my departure with a slightly uncomfortable smile, unsure whether they should say something. Another wishes me a quiet "good luck".

As the train pulls away, I gather up my things and try to decide what to do with them. Do I even still want them? Other passengers return to their conversations, their books, or their devices, no longer interested in the reason for the stop. Unsure where I will find another seat, I make my way through to the next carriage clutching the half-empty bag to my chest. I pause momentarily in the space between, where the sound of the train moving over the tracks fills my awareness. Wait here. Catch your breath. Calm down a little and stop worrying about the coffee stains on your clothes. No one cares. With a deep breath, I walk towards the next carriage. Immediately, heads turn to see who has caused the doors to slide open. They smile at me; one says "hello", another moves her bag so I can sit down at their table. With an awkward grin, I place my bag beneath my feet and settle into the conversation. I feel my breath slow down, my heart follows, some of the tension leaves my shoulders and jaw. I even laugh at a joke. I relax back into my seat with the knowledge I'll be alright here.'

Vignette: A Human Touch

Back in the bowels of the hospital for another procedure. After two weeks of shielding, I am glad to be out of the house, even if this feels like a dark, enclosed space to enter on a bright September morning.

Down the stone steps into the basement to the MRI room. The usual undressing and donning the hospital robe. After waiting a few weeks for this biopsy, the anxiety is mixed with relief that it is finally happening.

Unusually, there are quite a few people in the room when I enter. The previous occasion was only me and the radiographer. This time, there are three, maybe four, radiographers plus the consultant radiologist.

Face down on the cold, hard bed, with my breasts placed in their little compartments, I slid backwards into the machine. Instructed not to move, buzzer in hand in case I really cannot manage. The whirr of the MRI starts. For this particular procedure, they need to markup exactly the area under question and position a tube through my breast to be able to take the biopsy. Immediately, we have one false start as my breasts are too small to be accessed from the sternum side, nearest to the suspected tumour. They reset everything up and we go in again. The radiologist is embarrassed by this fact, and I just laugh and say it's not a problem; that lightens the mood.

It is cold in the room - the MRI needs to stay at a certain temperature. They wrap blankets around me wherever they can to keep me warm. I start to shiver a little; most likely brought on by the adrenaline in the four shots of local anaesthetic needed to numb the area before I can cope with the insertion of the tube -

the infamous piece of equipment we had waited for weeks to arrive from the suppliers in Belgium. I am starting to struggle. The shaking becomes quite distressing, as does the sensation of the tube being inserted into the outside edge of my breast - all the way through to reach that point near the sternum where they think there might be some more cancer. The gentle voices of the radiographers asking me to stay as still as possible because they need to be exact. I tell them that I understand.

Then a touch of a hand on my right shoulder blade. No gloves, nothing between each other. A gentle, compassionate stroke of my skin. To let me know that I am not alone. I start to cry. Not because I am sad but because I feel a release of all the barriers that COVID has put between us as human beings. The masks, the gloves, the distance. In that moment, when I need to feel somebody is there looking after me, that feeling of somebody else's warmth against my slightly shaking body allows the other sensations to melt away.

It takes a little while longer to perform the actual biopsy; this was the part that was aerosol-generating and had required me to isolate for two weeks before. Once that part is complete, they very carefully help me to turn over and lie on my back, staring up at the ceiling. The backlit picture of flowers, pink against a blue background, are there to distract. I am shaking so much and I am so cold, they provide no such diversion. One of the radiographers begins pressing against the outside edge of my left breast to stem the bleeding from where they had taken the biopsy. The other, the one who touched my shoulder, stays by my side to comfort me and explain what is going to happen next.

"It's going to take about 15 minutes to stop the bleeding, and then we'll get you up and make you a nice cup of sweet tea to raise your blood sugar. Then you can go home."

I am there for some time. It takes longer than expected to stop the bleeding, and then when I do finally get up, I need at least two cups of sweet tea and biscuits before I feel able to dress myself. As I stand up to do that, blood appears on the dressing on my left breast, so they lie me down once more. During all the time I've been there, there is so much warmth and care from the staff that the unpleasantness of what had preceded it already starts to fade away. Whilst drinking my tea, I message Paul to collect me. He ends up driving around the hospital waiting for me.

My overriding memory of this day is that touch on my bare shoulder. A tender moment to feel people care for you as an individual. The test will prove to be successful. Unfortunately, it reveals that I have two other types of cancer in that left breast, but the result comes back in time for the necessary surgery to be scheduled on the same date as the right mastectomy. There will be quite a lot of conversation about the procedure because it is so rarely done, and the radiologist who has performed it found it quite challenging.

This is the diagnostic that has kept me in limbo for weeks. That held my future health in uncertainty, awaiting the arrival of a piece of equipment. Waiting for a member of staff to come back from their holiday so we could schedule the appointment because they carried out this procedure so rarely that not all the radiologists were trained to do it. That one of the radiographers came over especially from the other hospital just to see the procedure performed because in the four years she had worked in breast screening she had never seen it done. All that fuss. All that attention and precision was worth it. My memory is that touch.

3

Letting Go; Finding Calm

"We have absolutely no control over what happens to us in life, but what we have paramount control over is how we respond to those events."

— *Dr Viktor E. Frankl, Professor of Neurology & Psychiatry, University of Vienna Medical School & Holocaust Survivor*

About five or six years ago now, I attended a Women in Business conference with my good friend Cecilia Costello, where a woman called Nina Joy spoke about her experiences with breast cancer. Now, as coincidence would have it, Cecilia had worked for Nina in her former corporate position in a bank. Like me, Cecilia had left her job in the corporate world after having her kids to pursue her dream and passion of photography. It's one of the things that drew us together when we met at the side of the court while our sons learnt to play tennis over ten years ago.

I have always remembered Nina's talk. At the time, it inspired me, as was its intention, to take control and action in my life. Nina used the analogy of a TV remote control as a way of viewing how to tackle a difficult situation - who has control of it and which buttons you choose to press. For Nina, events were running away from her as she received her terminal cancer diagnosis and was given six months to live. The medical team took over and told her what she needed to do. The medical team held the TV remote and intended to press play on what the next steps were. She acknowledged that she went home and freaked out for 24 hours before saying to herself, "What would I do if this was a business problem? How would I handle it? I wouldn't relinquish control to another person. So I'm not going to do the same with my life." Although I seem to recall her language was a touch more colourful at the time!

At this point, she wrestled back the remote and pressed PAUSE to give herself the space to decide what she wanted to do, not what she was necessarily being told to. Firstly, she researched the possible options available to her, from the conventional to the most outlandish. Consequently, Nina refused chemotherapy and the path well-trodden by others and pursued a variety of innovative and unconventional approaches. Her attitude was that if she only had six months left, she wouldn't spend them feeling rubbish, going through chemotherapy and still not surviving at the end of it - much to the dismay of the medics and her family.

This talk was over two years after she'd been given six months to live.

I've often reflected on that talk; brave and tough decisions were made, with no guarantee of the outcome. I took away the message that sometimes it is good to step off the track, pause and evaluate before moving ahead, that there are times when conventional wisdom may not be the right path for everyone. It is one of those stories I used to share with clients about how sometimes it's good to think more laterally about a problem. I guess it is all about choices, as so many things are. We must make our own choices because if we forfeit that right, we leave a void where someone else will choose for us.

It wasn't many days after my diagnosis that this talk came to the front of my mind. That feeling that I could simply hand myself over to the medical team and follow what they said. Now whilst I completely respect their experience and knowledge, there is always benefit in knowing what is right for you and what suits your own unique disposition. As a self-confessed control freak, I knew that handing over the control of my life to someone else was never going to sit comfortably with me.

How do you get a control freak to let go?

I have always been capable of responding well to situations and handling the curve balls life throws at me. My default is to attempt to optimise for every possible outcome, though - lots of scenario and contingency planning - what if, what if, what if. It drives my husband mad!

Scenario planning right now was not going to be a good thing for my head or my outlook on the situation. There were too many 'known unknowns' regarding my diagnosis, not to mention all the 'unknown, unknowns' that could be thrown at me along the way. Even for me, there was too much uncertainty to play with.

I needed to decide what the next right thing to do was. The single next step.

In the shock of finding out I had cancer, it was very easy to say that I had no obvious risk factors; that I was 'healthy' before. I was not overweight, had an active job and lifestyle, I ate well, I walked the dog, went to the gym, and in previous years, had trained for and taken part in triathlons. There was no history of breast cancer in my family. I could shrug my shoulders and call it bad luck.

But then there was a harsher reality.

This was a big, fat wake-up call. Even before a friend, Jo, called it out that she believed stress had caused cancer to take hold, the realisation was forming in my own mind. I had to acknowledge it in order to be able to move from that state of shock after the initial diagnosis.

Honestly, on and off since 2011 for sure, I lived extensive periods of my life like there was a sabre tooth tiger at the door, a hurricane in the back garden and Mrs Rochester living in the attic. I barely had time to clear up the mess left from the last hurricane before the next storm came around the corner, or the tiger got hungry again! This level of chronic stress was 'normal' to me. There were some classic tell-tale signs in the gastric problems that I had experienced over recent years and my history of a disrupted sleep pattern.

The issue was that I had not dealt with all the stress, and it had stayed in my body. I have proven to be adept at handling the actual stressors life throws at me, but I haven't taken the steps to fully work through the stress cycle and 'reset' my body back down to a baseline level. This led to an accumulation of 'stress' living in my body in various forms. My brain was set in survival mode, and although I was monitoring what was going on, I wasn't regulating my responses.

Most people are familiar with the 'fight or flight' response in our bodies but humour me while I give you my interpretation of what I know and how I apply it to my situation.

We now know so much more about how the body stores trauma. In his book, *The Body Keeps the Score: Mind, Brain and Body in the Transformation of Trauma*, Bessel van der Kolk explains the process by which people are unable to safely reset their nervous systems after a traumatic event and how the body continues in survival mode. He has a lovely explanation of the brain having a smoke detector - the amygdala - and a watchtower - the prefrontal cortex - and how knowing the difference between top-down and bottom-up regulation aids the understanding and treating of traumatic stress. Top-down regulation improves the ability of the watchtower to monitor your body's sensation, say through mindfulness meditation and yoga, whilst bottom-up requires recalibrating the autonomic nervous system (ANS) that can be achieved through breath, touch or movement. As van der Kolk points out, 'breathing is one of the few body functions under both conscious and autonomic control'. Rather than taking breathing for granted, maybe we should treat it with greater respect and care.

I'll take a step back to go into a bit more detail if I may. The oldest part of the brain, often referred to as the reptilian brain, is in the brain stem - where the spinal cord enters the skull. It controls all our essential life-sustaining functions. Then we have the limbic system - the amygdala, hippocampus, hypothalamus and thalamus - which houses our emotions and monitors danger along with the brain stem. The key task is to look after our welfare and protect us from danger or threat. This 'emotional brain' tends to jump to conclusions and initiate pre-programmed 'escape' plans - so fight or flight - where the automatic muscular and physiological reactions start before we consciously catch up. Then we have the prefrontal cortex. The frontal lobes are what make us human - giving us the gift of language, abstract thought, the ability to take in huge quantities of information and give meaning to it, to plan, reflect, imagine and act out future scenarios.

When sensory information arrives in our brain, in the thalamus, it stirs it all up and then sends it off to both the amygdala - the smoke detector - and the medial prefrontal cortex - the watchtower - via the hippocampus and anterior cingulate. The amygdala path is the fast track, so it responds to a threat and has signalled to release stress hormones, which include adrenaline and cortisol before the rational brain has a chance to interpret the message. When it operates correctly, the watchtower can see if you are responding to a false alarm (or not) and restore balance by taking the appropriate action - which may be to halt the stress response. The watchtower gives that ability to 'hover calmly and objectively' as van der Kolk puts it and to take our time to respond appropriately whilst damping the automatic reactions. Post-trauma, an overintense interpretation of threat by the amygdala and/or a weakened processing system in the brain's higher centres, can result in losing control of automatic responses seen as blow-ups or shutdowns in response to relatively innocuous situations.

I really like this explanation of the smoke detector and the watchtower because although I've never suffered the level of trauma they talk about in the book, you can see how that traumatic response can scale down to a life situation where you are always on 'simmer'.

I was living in a situation where certain life events had resulted in me developing a pattern of responding, and as these neural circuits consistently fired together, it became my default setting. Although I would rationalise and consider the outcomes, I wasn't doing this in such a way to create the appropriate top-down regulation, nor was I applying timely intervention through breathing exercises, for example, to be able to intervene with the bottom-up regulation.

The brain has a natural negativity bias. To quote Rick Hanson and Richard Mendius from their book *Buddha's Brain: The Practical Neuroscience of Happiness, Love, And Wisdom* -'The negativity bias fosters or intensifies other unpleasant emotions, such as anger, sorrow, depression, guilt and shame. It highlights past losses and failures; it downplays present abilities and it exaggerates future obstacles. Consequently, the mind continually tends to render unfair verdicts about a person's character, conduct and possibilities. The weight of those judgements can really wear you down.'

Wow! Judgement - I've expended so much energy on judgement -

of myself and those around me. Hanson goes on to describe what he calls the 'second dart' - our reactions to the 'first dart' of physical or mental discomfort. So, you stub your toe - which hurts - but then you follow it up by getting angry about 'who left the chair in the wrong place?' Frequently, we fire off these second darts when there was no first physical dart at all, adding to our discomfort or 'suffering' as Hanson likes to call it. The sympathetic nervous system (SNS) response to threat or danger sets off a cascade of events in the ANS that prepare major organs and muscle groups to fight or flee whilst the hypothalamus acts in its role of regulator of the endocrine system by prompting the release of adrenaline and cortisol. While once this was necessary for survival, the chronic stressors of life come at a cost to our bodies.

Living a 'life on simmer' that we push into stress by continually throwing second darts coupled with the pace of modern society leads to ongoing arousal of the sympathetic nervous system and adrenal glands. In that place, you are not focusing resources on longer-term health, such as your immune system or mood, as you are in the bog of the short-term crisis. The negative physical and mental consequences follow. Welcome to the parasympathetic nervous system (PNS), which is the other branch of the ANS that promotes the 'rest and digest' system and produces a sense of relaxation and contentment. This, surprising as it may seem, is the normal resting state of our bodies, brain and mind. Both the SNS and PNS are activated when we inhale and exhale, respectively. That is why we feel good if we take some even, long steady breaths - both alert and alive and grounded and calm. We don't need to shut down the SNS but keep the system in a state of balance. And that takes practice. Hanson suggests that a good aim is 'a baseline of mainly PNS arousal with mild SNS activation for vitality, combined with occasional SNS spikes for major opportunities and threats.' There is, of course, a lot more to it than that, but you get the idea. One final comment from Hanson's book is that of focusing on 'the law of little things' - lots of small moments of practice to replace the default reactions and structures with more happiness, love and wisdom.

The thing was, I knew so much about this already. It is so easy to know things and yet not unquestionably do them. I had been trying to implement change, but I'd never quite turned the corner for it to make enough of a difference. That wasn't to say I wasn't doing anything of value, but the consistency was lacking, so I never quite got to the point of being consciously competent. I should also add that I did know this was happening, but I was on a merry-go-round that I jumped off occasionally but kept returning to out of habit. Perhaps there was always the thought that I could do it later, so I hadn't truly put it front and centre.

Once I identified what was going on for me, I accepted it. Feeling guilty or beating myself up about it only serves to continue and reinforce the pattern of firing those second darts and not finding safety. It is what it is. I am where I am. There's no time like the present. And the present is all I have. There was no hiding from this - this whirlwind had hit me and swept me into Cancer Land. It wasn't going away.

Nina's talk was all about what you could control. What I needed to learn straightaway was, in reality, what was out of my control that I needed to let go of?

I cannot control what is already in my body.

I cannot control what they are going to find.

I cannot control what the medical treatment options are.

I cannot control how COVID restrictions will impact the process.

I cannot control whether the cancer has already spread in my body.

I cannot control how effective the treatment will be.

I cannot control the random events that mean it might recur later.

Let's not worry about any of that for a moment. What might I be able to influence? Let's look at what positive action I can take at this moment to make a difference to how I feel about this, how I cope with it and how I might give my body the best chance to deal with it.

I can control what I put in my body,

I can control what thoughts are in my head

I can control the language I use and what I tell myself about what is going on.

I can control what I do with my body activity-wise

I can control how I choose to handle the day-to-day stuff that comes my way.

This exercise gave me further clarity about what I wanted to do, and which buttons I wanted to press on the remote control while I waited for all the tests and results to reach my full diagnosis.

My gut and my head - that was where I was going to start.

Being kind to my gut

My gut has always been one of the weak spots for me. Right back to 1998, when I started with irritable bowel syndrome (IBS) during my time in a corporate job, if I was going to show signs that my body was not coping with life, that is where it would show up. I took action to deal with it on each occasion in the best way I was able to. When I left that job in 2000, the IBS cleared up almost instantly, which struck home for the first time that it was a stress-related symptom. The decision to leave that career was about far more than my stomach issues - I was burned out and suffering from depression. This was a hugely significant moment in my life; I learnt a lot about myself, what I wanted and what was important to me.

As far as the IBS goes, I was fine for years after that. I had changed my environment and, to a certain extent, how I dealt with life. The life that I went into after parting waves with my corporate career - some time off to get my head in check, then I started at university to study physiotherapy - was markedly less stressful than the life before. I was able to manage what I found in life's path. Well, for a while, at least.

Fast forward 15 years, where life events compounded to a head by 2015. I was taken ill very suddenly with what turned out to be Erosive Gastritis - a condition where the lining of the stomach has been damaged, so the stomach acid damages the stomach tissue itself.

Following this, I made some immediate changes to my diet and experimented with a few options before giving up gluten completely in 2017. It was quite the Herculean effort as I loved my bread! For some reason, I went cold turkey on everything choosing a weekend when I was travelling to Dublin to assist Diane Lee on a physio course. Boy was I unwell. I had what is known as a Herxheimer reaction as my body detoxified from the gluten. After three weeks of this, there was no way I was going to undo all this effort, and I have stuck with it pretty much ever since.

I tinkered with my diet again in 2018, this time working with someone on a restrictive diet - no caffeine, alcohol, dairy, sugar, processed foods - over the course of about five months. It certainly showed me that I had the willpower to give stuff up - the accountability of having to report back to someone certainly helped with this. Although I did stick to it, it never quite hit the mark. I managed to stick with some of the changes - stayed off the gluten and the caffeine and reduced the sugar substantially. The alcohol crept back in, as it tends to - I would rely on this crutch, both as a 'reward or celebration' for something good or a pick-me-up after a bad day. Either way, it was used to take the edge off the weight of living.

My brutal friend, Jo, (remember, the one who called out the stress as the cause of the cancer?) gave me the name of a nutritionist, Dawn Waldron, who specialises in working with women with breast cancer. After all the eating approaches I had tried in the recent past, I wanted to do this properly. I made the necessary arrangements to speak with Dawn and having decided I trusted her and that we could work together, I proceeded to get some tests done to discover the starting point.

Since I was already open to the idea of changing my diet because of the previous changes I'd made, Dawn felt I should go straight in and have the nutrigenetics test. This test is designed to understand how your gene expression impacts the way you respond to diet and lifestyle. That is how your genes affect your nutrient requirement, your ability to detoxify chemicals and drugs, your antioxidant capacity, and hormone and neurotransmitter levels. Dawn looks at the results in relation to breast cancer risk and the factors that relate to your individual breast cancer diagnosis.

In my case, the cancer was oestrogen-receptor-positive - which means that the oestrogen in my body feeds the cancer. Dawn explained to me how certain metabolic processes are key to the detoxification of oestrogen and how my unique gene expression may not enable my body to perform this properly. The test would take a few weeks to come back, but in the meantime, she gave me the basics of what I needed to be doing to best support myself.

I love all this stuff! My conversation with Dawn to review my results when they arrived was illuminating and shed light on various significant factors that I could not doubt. In fact, they were so close to the reality of how I 'am'.

The test found, amongst other things, that I may be unusually sensitive to adrenaline and also slow to break it down with the double whammy of reduced levels of the inhibitory neurotransmitter GABA. In the brain, GABA activity has a calming effect. Inhibitory neurotransmitters like GABA block certain brain signals and decrease nervous system activity.

"You are likely to have an exaggerated fight-or-flight response to stressful situations," Dawn said.

I burst out laughing. "I didn't need a test to tell me that! Anyone that knows me well would tell you that."

All my friends agreed, of course, when we shared the joke later.

The other key factor was that adrenaline promotes the production of the Aromatase enzyme, which in turn increases oestrogen production. Given that I had oestrogen-receptor-positive breast cancer, I needed to make changes to discourage this cycle.

With that knowledge, it certainly focused the mind to implement the changes that Dawn recommended. I needed to avoid putting more adrenaline into my body to fuel that response - no caffeine, no alcohol, no stress!

The diet - or 'energy management plan' as Dawn called it - was very specific to my circumstances and the results of the nutrigenetics test. The premise is to manage your energy intake in the form of glucose to reduce the fuel for the cancer, alongside removing or adding the necessary food groups, vitamins and minerals as required. Having adapted my diet in the past, I didn't find this too hard to do. It gave me some control. I feel positive about the changes I've made, not to mention that I actually feel and look really well on it. The plan has altered since I completed the active treatment of chemotherapy and radiotherapy, but what I am doing now, I can continue.

This does make it sound quite easy, which at the time it was as I was so focused on looking after myself, and the fear about the cancer was, unsurprisingly, an outstandingly strong motivator. This is me giving up something that I really used to enjoy. I liked a drink. I liked the taste of it - a crisp glass of chilled white wine on a summer's day, a cold beer after a day's skiing, a warming glass of red with a delicious meal or snuggled up watching a movie, and a vibrant, spicy G&T in a huge balloon glass with ice, some fancy tonic and whatever was the trendy garnish of the moment. I loved them all. More to the point, I took pleasure in getting drunk. I cannot lie about this. By this, I don't just mean a little bit tipsy, where the world becomes a little bit fuzzy around the edges as the alcohol takes its effect. No, I mean consciously getting full-blown drunk. The times when you lose all inhibition and have no cares. You know you are doing it and it feels liberating to let it all go. It wasn't something I did that often since having kids, but there were those occasions when we were out that I would allow myself to be swept along by the waves. That wonderful feeling of completely letting go of yourself on a dancefloor, dancing like no one was watching. There was that fine line between being that happy, uninhibited 'drunk' and almost observing your behaviour and knowing what was going on, to the tipping point where you lost control and felt unwell. Fortunately, I stayed on the right side of the 'unwell' line most of the time, although that is not to say that I did not suffer from hangovers. I can safely say that I am not missing the hangovers!

The trick, I have discovered, is not to dwell on the things I have eliminated but to have almost a dispassionate attitude toward those things that are not good for me. Once the alcohol and caffeine habits were broken, I gained an understanding of myself and what is good for me versus what I actually used to like. To think of those times when I was fuelled on coffees and those episodes in my life when I was drinking to excess. Through all those coping mechanisms that we put in place, we lose a sense of control and no longer see that we have the power to change it. I reinforce my new thought patterns by frequently revisiting why I am doing this and articulating it out loud, either for my own benefit or in a conversation with others. I've probably become a bit of a bore, and because of COVID, I haven't had many opportunities to test how this sober life sits for me in a more social setting. However, at this moment in time, I feel in control, calm and content about my gut, and I can tell you it feels pretty amazing.

It's all in your head

Next on the agenda was to get control over my thoughts. The first thing to get my head in check was making some work decisions. I needed to get my ducks in a row on the practical aspects like the practice. There was a good deal of contingency planning to do - well, emergency planning was probably a better description. I made arrangements at work for my prolonged absence. This became the ultimate 'Out Of Office' protocol. There was no way of knowing whether this would work, but necessity is the mother of invention and all that. There was no choice, so we had to let it play out, at least for a few months. There may come a point when I would have to pull the plug, but for now, this was the best way to handle it.

I won't pretend that I didn't want to just give up on work straightaway. It suddenly felt so unimportant. Such a contrast to those early days and weeks of lockdown when I couldn't hold back the tears at the thought of losing the business. The thoughts of how much of me I had put into it and that I couldn't let it go. Right now, I could. It was in its proper place. The priority levels had been reset in a spectacular fashion. As I let go, the business slowly started to lose its hold over me, and I started to regain the control over it as an entity - not a breathing, living thing. Let it go.

Next, I made an extremely conscious decision to be positive. I pretty much said to myself, "I want to be one of those people who stays as cheerful and bright as possible through all of this". Not least because I did not want to live with someone who was gloomy all the time.

In order to do that, though, I needed to get really clear about my emotions and what I was feeling. The emotional shock of the diagnosis had kept my anger in check over the first few days, but it was there and I knew it. As luck would have it, I listened to a podcast with Marc Brackett - the Director at the Yale Center for Emotional Intelligence - talking about his recent book *Permission to Feel. Unlocking the Power of Emotions to Help our Kids, Ourselves and our Society Thrive*. Talk about hearing what you need to hear when you need to hear it! I bought the book immediately.

He talks about the system he developed to understand and master emotion - known by the acronym RULER. This covers the skills of **R**ecognising, **U**nderstanding, **L**abelling, **E**xpressing and **R**egulating emotion. Within the book, there is a terrific grid called the Mood Meter, designed to chart every feeling a human can experience based on two scales - Pleasantness and Energy - and colour coded to reflect the emotional state. The top right quadrant is yellow - high pleasantness and high energy - motivated, hopeful, happy. The top left is red - low pleasantness but high energy - angry, irritated, stressed. The bottom right is green - high pleasantness but low energy - restful, calm, content. Finally, the bottom left is blue - low pleasantness and low energy - discouraged, lonely, fatigued. There are 25 emotions in each quadrant so there is plenty to go at.

Why have I taken the time to explain all this in so much detail? Well, because this grid became pivotal in understanding and managing my emotions. It confirmed how I had been predominantly living in the red zone, so working on letting go of that anger was a huge one for me. It gave me a much wider vocabulary to add greater nuance to how I felt each day - rather than simply happy, sad or pissed off, to quote Brené Brown. First thing every day, I would check in with myself - how do I feel today? I started to journal about it. I set myself the goal of not simply saying "I'm alright" or "I'm okay" when people asked me how I was. I started to sense I was gaining greater insight into what I was feeling and how I might be able to intervene when the pull of those red emotions might draw me back again.

Most importantly, as it said on the cover, it undoubtedly gave me permission to feel what I was feeling. To allow myself to experience whatever was going on but not dwell in the dark places too long. And as I started to slowly slide across the grid with my emotions, like ice melting on a lake, I found myself in the blue zone, then the green.

It was not, of course, without effort. What I have learnt through all of this experience, though, is what helps me to move into that space where I feel calm, content and at ease. It evolves and changes but back at the start of this journey, I turned to a few things. Walking with Jess, my dog, hypnotherapy, breathwork and the start of meditation.

Walking was easy and a no-brainer if I'm honest. With minimal things to do for work, I had all the time I wanted to walk - so I did. Being able to walk with Jess and not having to think I was rushing back for anything was such a treat. It was August, and as I had missed most of the lovely weather so far that spring and summer, I took every opportunity to be outside, whether that was walking or sitting in the garden reading and often snoozing.

I didn't feel up to much else in the way of exercise since the scans and biopsies left me feeling quite sore. Although I tried some online yoga classes, I couldn't get my body to work or feel good about it. There was something interfering with me being able to connect with and coordinate my body. So I let it go for a while.

Instead, I focused on breathing (or pranayama as it is known in yoga), meditation classes and journaling. Meditation was something I had started to play with during the early months of lockdown when my local yoga studio had run some really great programmes to support people. It was a two-week challenge to get you into the regular habit of meditating. I already knew how much benefit I achieved through hypnotherapy, so I had always been keen to make more of regular meditation. In the past, I'd messed about with doing five minutes on a morning before getting out of bed, but since spring, I had been sitting in a quiet space and following the guided session and recordings. Now I started really taking it seriously. I found that I could meditate without the help of a recording by working through the pranayama practice. The yoga breath work is fantastic.

The breathing gave me the way into my body. A way to tap into my parasympathetic nervous system and soothe my tired body. The various pranayama breathing techniques I had learnt in the guided sessions, I put into my own daily practice - starting at ten minutes and then building from there. Over time, it gradually became automatic to start the day this way, and I looked forward to it. As my whole system calmed down and settled more often towards a place of greater ease and peacefulness, I found that I could focus more clearly and concentrate for longer during the meditation. My life was typically so busy and full, and I spent so much time talking to people each day through my work that this quiet time to myself became a welcome change. A calm place where I learnt to be, to quieten my racing mind. The beauty for me was that I could start to recreate more of how I felt with the hypnotherapy.

Hypnotherapy

My journey with hypnotherapy started back in 2014, initially to attempt to get control over my terrible sleep patterns. I'd tried other things. Having found Neuro-Linguistic Programming (NLP) to be beneficial in the past, I went there first, but to no avail on this occasion. My head was racing at such a fast pace I just could not get what I needed out of the sessions. In addition, I felt so mentally and emotionally exhausted after each one that it felt like it was doing more harm than good.

With a well-established pattern of waking in the early hours most days and often struggling to get off to sleep most nights, by the time we got to 2014, I essentially knew no different. After having two children, I was regularly waking at 1am, despite the rest of the house sleeping soundly. The story I tell myself is that after my youngest took four years to decide to sleep through the night, my body never got the memo that it was over and kept helpfully waking me up each night to check on the world. Now, I'm not blaming him, far from it. As any parent knows, you do what you have to do to get sleep with a couple of kids, and we had settled into a routine that worked as best as it could for us. I had moved so far past the judgement of others as to why Matthew would not sleep. There was equally no rhyme or reason as to why one night, shortly after his fourth birthday, he slept all night and then continued to do so. The reality was that I had a problem long before either of my children showed up; two pregnancies and night-time feeding did have a role in disrupting my sleep for many years, but the cycle was entrenched before then.

By 2014, we were two years on from Matthew sleeping soundly each night and I'm not sure I had really registered it was an issue. As a working mum, you get so proficient at surviving with little to no sleep you forget what it is like not to feel jaded each day. A chance conversation with a regular physiotherapy client presented the possibility to me that I might have a problem. She suggested I speak to the doctor. The only solution offered to me were sleeping pills, and the suggestion that I should try to be 'less stressed', along with the usual advice about a pre-bed routine of no booze, caffeine, reduced screen time and a hot bath.

"You are a classic insomniac."

Until the doctor used that term, I had never once thought of myself as having insomnia in all the years of poor sleep (which, when I worked it out, was about 15 years). I did not adopt the label either. Writing me off with a prescription for pills was not the solution I wanted or required. So I continued to play with various and ever-increasingly more fanatical bedtime routines. A further conversation with a new client led me to see his wife, Elaine, for my first hypnotherapy session. She was a former mental health nurse who had recently moved into this field.

As a paediatric consultant, my client admitted, "I'm the biggest sceptic going about hypnotherapy, but I've tried it and it really does seems to work."

Never one to shirk new experiences, and quite frankly, I had exhausted all other options, I gave her a call. I was excited to try something completely different. One of my better decisions!

Hypnotherapy is not what you see on stage or television. I understood enough to know that I was not going to be dancing around her room like a chicken. It serves to take you into a relaxed, trance-like state where your brain is open to suggestions presented to it by the therapist based upon whatever it is you are working on.

After taking time to first understand the problem, we embark on the actual treatment. I lie on the wonderful couch, and she commences the relaxation and the countdown from 1 to 10 to take me into a deep trance-like state. This often involves imagining walking down a beautiful staircase to a place of calm and peace; it is the most wonderful thing in the world to me. After the first session, I distinctly remember having to pop into our local store to buy something for our evening meal. I was walking around thinking, *oh my goodness, I have absolutely nothing going on in my head.* An unfamiliar sensation to say the least, but I loved how it felt. I wanted to experience more.

The power of hypnotherapy for me is the ability to switch off that continuous stream of thoughts that run through my head. As I have continued to practice meditation since my cancer diagnosis, I can honestly say that my head is often quiet, and it is a joy, however, back in 2014, that was not the case. Nonetheless, as I attended further sessions, and learnt and applied self-hypnosis techniques among other things, I regained control over my sleep and my life was transformed.

I went from being unable to get to sleep easily and frequently getting up at 3am to do my ironing to sleeping like a baby every night. At the time, I was training for my first standard distance triathlon, and when I started going out for early morning runs, having had a full night's sleep, I realised how exhausted I had been for the previous goodness knows how many years.

Hypnotherapy has become a cornerstone for me. Sometimes that means having a session, and sometimes I access the techniques - visualisation, breathing, anchors - to steer myself back on course. I don't think of it as 'fixing the problem' but rather an exploration into where I am and what I best need at that point. There is no magic bullet. I still have to apply what I know – just do the thing!

Working on understanding my feelings and emotions was helping, and I felt calmer each day with the breath work and meditation, but I needed to tap deeper into my subconscious. I needed to suggest to it that I would cope with the daunting things that were coming up for me - the results from the MRI-guided biopsy to confirm or otherwise if I had cancer in the other breast, the actual surgery and beyond. I needed Elaine to guide me through this so I could manage the demons lurking in my head. Thankfully, she kindly agreed to do some sessions over the telephone, and these kept me grounded and boosted my positivity during the subsequent months.

Living one day at a time

This is a tough one for me as I like to plan and think ahead. However, the sheer exhaustion washing over me meant I couldn't comprehend planning too far ahead in those first few weeks. As a result, there was nothing else I could do in those days prior to the surgery. I lived from one appointment to the next. A short while after my diagnosis, we met up with some good friends, one of whom offered this pragmatic piece of advice.

"Don't worry before the event. When you have a procedure with a two-week delay for results, don't start worrying about the results two weeks before the actual test. That ends up as a month of worry!" Easier said than done, but somehow, I managed it. I didn't research hormone medications, radiotherapy, follow-up tests, CT scans, or all the possible future scenarios - I focused solely on the next hurdle whilst living as the healthiest version of me I could.

In between, I resolved to make the most of the time this unfortunate turn of events had given me. I sat in the garden and read my books, listened to podcasts, and took the odd nap. For the first time in a long time, no one really expected anything of me. It was both liberating and empowering.

Gradually I shifted into dealing with one day at a time and finding pleasure in the smallest of things each day so that I could end it with a smile. A routine began to develop, starting with my morning breath work and meditation, which, coupled with walking Jess and investing time in cooking healthier meals, created a framework I could hang my day on. Compared to where I'd come from, this routine felt spacious and open, with plenty of opportunity to choose to sit and take a moment - to pause and breathe.

Despite this life-threatening diagnosis hanging over me like a dark cloud, moments where I felt relief and ease were plentiful.

A calm settled over us as I waited for the final results. I felt as well as I possibly could. Only a few days before my scheduled surgery, the MRI-guided biopsy results came back positive for three 1mm Invasive Tubular Carcinomas and Non-Invasive Ductal cancer in my left breast. There are only four types of breast cancer, so I had certainly made a good job of it! Despite this not being the news I had hoped for, Nathaniel injected, once again, some much-needed humour into the situation.

"What is it with you, Mum? Are you playing cancer bingo or something?"

———————

'We're moving along at speed now. I feel less awkward as we've spent the time chatting and swapping anecdotes since the train set off. Yes, I am going to be alright here I repeat in my head. I can sit back and try to make the most of the journey. Outside the window the countryside sweeps past my eyes. From the window seat, I rest my head back against the chair and withdraw from the chatter to capture a quiet moment for myself. There is still a long way to go. There will be plenty of time to re-join the conversation.'

———————

Serenity Prayer

"Grant me the serenity to accept the things I cannot change, courage to change the things I can, and wisdom to know the difference."

Vignette: On the Count of 10...

"On the count of 10, you will be back with me, wide, wide awake and feeling completely normal for you..."

These are the words the hypnotherapist says to bring me out of my trance-like state. Right from the very first time I visited Elaine, this line has made me smile as I rise to the surface from that wonderful state of calmness and being.

Normal for me! What is normal for me? Or anyone else, for that matter. Who gets to decide what is normal? One thing I know for sure is that what is normal for me is not 'normal' for most people. I am comfortable with that now.

> *"You use hypnosis not as a cure but as a means of establishing a favourable climate in which to learn."*
>
> *– Milton Erickson, American Psychiatrist*

As the quote says, it 'establishes a favourable climate to learn'. Hypnotherapy opened the door for me to other possibilities. Having this in my toolkit has certainly assisted me in being able to start to master meditation. It has given me the belief that I can quieten my mind and take pleasure from being in that place. I'm not missing out or underperforming if I make space in my day to be quiet.

When I originally started yoga over 20 years ago, although I enjoyed relaxation at the end, I never appreciated that I needed to keep in the present and not allow my mind to shoot off to what I was doing next. I never took the next step to make it a practice. I am not sure whether this is something I would have tried at that age. With the benefit of hindsight, I regret I did not explore meditation more; if I had been open to it then perhaps I could have moved through this life in a different way. I held some fairly tight beliefs about the sort of person I was, unfortunately adopting plenty of labels from others along the way. If only I'd known.

Through hypnotherapy, I learned to focus on Elaine's voice, which guided me to calm and quieten those thoughts. As I practised self-hypnosis each day - counting myself down the steps to focus on something when I got there - I began to cultivate an understanding of what to do.

I am sharing this experience if you are someone who thinks you can't meditate, that it's not for you - your mind is too busy to ever stop! Is there the possibility you might be uncomfortable with the thoughts that do emerge if you sit quietly?

My invitation is to give it a try. You'll never know unless you try. Who knows? Maybe you'll surprise yourself. It could be for 'someone like you'.

'Someone like you' - these words have stayed with me for many years following a comment made to me by a woman who I might have described as a friend.

"I wouldn't have thought that it [hypnotherapy] would work for someone like you."

The comment was made during a conversation where I shared my joy and enthusiasm at what hypnotherapy had given me. It really got under my skin. I felt so judged by the statement. Momentarily, it robbed me of the delight I was trying to describe. At the time, I took it personally, and it hurt my feelings. A lot.

"What's wrong with someone like me?"

This was not the first time, and it wouldn't be the last, that people passed such comments. For so long, I have taken on labels and opinions - 'Type A personality', 'You're so stressed all the time', 'Can't you chill out a bit?', 'You're always on the go', 'You do too much'.

Fair enough, there was an element of truth in the observations. However, on occasion, the comments were made about me being me - enthusiastic, motivated and passionate about something – then I felt dented, inadequate, small.

It took me until my 40s to work with the right coaches and mentors to learn that I could be myself. Who gets to say what type of person we are? Why does someone else get to judge me as good, bad or ugly? If I have lots of energy that I want to invest in something, then that's for me to decide.

It's all about context. When I started to attend leadership and development conferences and workshops where the learning environment was biased towards positive ideas and feedback, my perspective of myself began to alter.

In one exercise, where the other participants did not know me and had nothing to gain or lose from the interaction, the descriptors of 'Inspiring Energiser' and 'Queen Bee' arose. Initially, neither of these sat well with me as they seemed to reinforce all the bad things I had been told about myself.

"Not at all," was the response. "These are great characteristics to have. Your energy and enthusiasm and love of life are infectious. Don't lose that or see it as a negative."

I began to recalibrate what I thought of myself. The past judgements started to fade.

Now I am proud to be someone like me. I get to decide what I try and what I practice in my life; what works for me, and who I want to be.

This experience has really brought out the two sides of me - the courage, strength and resilience counterbalanced with calm, acceptance and peace. Discovering the latter started with my exploration of hypnotherapy and is developing as I practice yoga and meditation.

As I reach the count of 10 now, I am back in the room as a different 'normal' to what I was that first time in 2014. The calm space persists and exists beyond the therapy couch.

Right now, I love being in the quiet space in my head. I am glad the crazy grand prix can take a pit stop. I know what I need to do to create that space for myself. This is not the end of the Inspiring Energiser or Queen Bee, though!

Throughout my cancer treatment, I have been working on projects - not least writing this book – and exploring ideas and new places. I have let my imagination run free and imagined a contrasting version of myself and my life, where I can balance out the calm and the courage. The being and the doing. I never want to lose who I am. My passion and energy for life, new experiences and challenges. What I have learned is how to cultivate and nurture myself so that I can be all of it. Hypnotherapy was my way in; it was the door I chose to open to find an environment in which to learn.

4

The Beginning of the Beginning

"We must be willing to let go of the life we planned so as to have the life that is waiting for us."

— *Joseph Campbell, American Writer*

Surgery day arrived. Monday the 14th of September 2020. For eight weeks, I had waited for this operation. The results came through from the MRI-guided biopsy just the week before to say that not only did I have Lobular Breast Cancer in my right breast, but they also found Invasive Tubular Carcinoma and Non-Invasive Ductal cancer in my left. I had four days to process the fact that I was having surgery on both sides. Over the weeks since my initial diagnosis, I had come to terms with the idea that I was losing the right breast and having an immediate reconstruction with an implant. We discussed, deliberated the prospect of having a new, fake boob and, quite often, joked about sizes and shapes! Now the day had arrived, and it felt exceedingly real and not terribly amusing at all.

I turned to hypnotherapy to prepare myself for how I might handle the surgery and its aftermath. Elaine suggested the idea of viewing the surgery as the beginning of the beginning. Not the loss of my right breast. Not something to be fearful about. To see it as the start of me getting better. In theory, after this surgery there would be no more cancer in my body; the surgeon would have removed everything. This sounded good to me. To awaken and feel I was at the start of something new; then I could look forward.

That said, I still had to get through the actual surgery. That morning was challenging, to say the least. All the cancer surgery was performed at the local, private hospital, the Yorkshire Clinic, the designated green ward during COVID. This was fortunate since it was only a five-minute drive from my house. However, before the surgery, I needed to visit two other hospitals in Bradford prior to arriving at the Yorkshire clinic. Bearing in mind where we were at this point in time, my husband, Paul, was not allowed to go into any of the hospitals with me. Firstly, we drove to St Luke's, a familiar destination as the breast clinic is based there, to have a mammogram. They had to insert a wire into my left breast to mark where the tumours were. Mammograms are horrible; we know this. Trying to screen so close to the sternum with small breasts and accurately enough to insert a wire into an extremely small area is a whole other ballgame. I think we had five attempts at squashing my breast into the mammogram - between those cold, hard plates. A local anaesthetic was given so they could insert the wire.

I've come to learn over this journey that my body does not get on well with the adrenaline in local anaesthetics. After discovering I have an increased sensitivity to it, everything made sense. In the moment, it was unsettling and a little scary. To feel out of control of my body before the day had begun. On top of being incredibly uncomfortable in the scanner, I was shaking too. I started to cry. I was already anxious about the surgery, and I was not prepared for this pre-procedure at all. The lovely women in the radiography department were kind, thoughtful and terribly apologetic but also matter of fact. They had to get the wire in. Over an hour later than I should have left the building, I returned to the car. Next, we drove to the Bradford Royal Infirmary (BRI), to the Nuclear Medicine department, down in the bowels of the hospital again, where I had been for my MRI a couple of weeks before. This time it was for a sentinel lymph node injection to help the surgeon identify which lymph nodes should be removed. Quick technical bit - this involves injecting a dye or radioactive tracer liquid into the nipple area. During the operation itself, the surgeon uses a special instrument to see which lymph nodes it travels to first. These nodes are the sentinel nodes. The surgeon then removes the nodes and sends them out for evaluation. Part of me was so interested in the science, and the other part wished it felt simpler.

So in tears, uncomfortable and late, I arrived at BRI. Fortunately, I was seen quite quickly, but I kept repeating to the staff, "Can somebody ring the surgeon to tell her I'm running really late?"

I don't know whether that phone call ever happened. Needless to say, in the car driving from Bradford back to Bingley, I was considerably distressed. Paul drove around the turning circle outside the Yorkshire clinic to drop me off. The COVID screening in reception was the last thing I needed that day. This ritual had become tiresome to me each time I attended appointments here. I knew it was a necessity that none of us wanted, and I tried to answer the questions, but inside I wanted to shout at them, "You do know I've got cancer, right? It says so on your form. They're cutting my right breast off this morning. Let me in so I can get this over with." I tried to keep this bottled up. The poor guy was only doing his job.

"Oh, we're glad to see you. We've all been twiddling our thumbs for the past hour or so!" Ms Tait was jovial as she entered my room. I smiled back and apologised for keeping them all waiting.

There was a knowing that passed between us. She'd been here so many times before with other women. There was no need to say more.

"Just glad that you're here. Let's get you sorted."

Shortly after, I walked across the hall into the theatre. The bright lights and clean white surfaces were offset by the blue and green scrubs of the staff. As they guided me to sit on the table, the theatre nurse softly asked me how I was.

I burst into tears. Proper tears. Sobbing. Shoulder shaking. It all came out, from that morning, from everything that had happened those past eight weeks, all of it. They didn't get drawn into it, but with tenderness, they said, "let's get you laid down." As the anaesthetist gently took my hand to insert the cannula and placed the mask over my face, I drifted away.

The next lights I saw were those of the recovery room. I had the sense of feeling alright - both physically and emotionally. Over the years, I've had some reasonably interesting recoveries due to low blood pressure. Not today. I didn't feel sick or dizzy. I just felt there. It was done. It was over. The cancer had been removed.

Back in my room, I sat up in bed. The nurses came in and out to see me. I sensed I felt alright with the world. There were various text messages from people asking me how I was, and I replied to my husband and maybe a couple of others. It wasn't until I received a message from my eldest son, Nathaniel, asking, 'how's the new boob?' that I thought to have a look. 'Oh, I still have a breast!' Partially covered in dressings, and looking a little bit bruised and discoloured, but it appeared okay. That was it then. It was over. Relief. Calm. I could look forward.

I spent a couple of days in the hospital, enjoying the peace and quiet. I had my book to read, I messaged people, and had a couple of conversations, but I wasn't really in the mood to talk out loud. I enjoyed the space. There was nothing I had to do. No visitors were allowed because of COVID, and I was comfortable with that.

I managed well with the pain medication and with being woken up regularly through the night to check my blood pressure, which stayed low. There was the headroom to come to terms with it all. I felt like I was on the mend to use that rather old-fashioned phrase.

During those two days, I posted something publicly for the first time on Facebook to say where I was and what had happened. The response was overwhelming. Kind, thoughtful, generous messages from people. Some of whom knew I was having the surgery, many who had no idea I was even unwell. Telling the world, or at least my little corner of it, felt like a big milestone - this is what just happened to me.

The beginning of the beginning. Once I went home, I had a few steady days to ease myself back to some kind of reality. It was tricky to negotiate life with a chest drain in and keep it away from the dog! I took short walks with her and my son - I couldn't take her out by myself because I couldn't hold the lead. I tried to stick to my rehab, that voice in my head reminding me of everything I would say to my physio clients about consistency and building good daily habits.

"Now it's time to actually show up, Jacqui, and take some of your own medicine. You do not want a frozen shoulder. Start small, but attempt it every day, even if it's only one rep of each exercise." Tough love, perhaps, but I am grateful for that tenacious spirit now.

I was due to see the surgeon two weeks later for my pathology results. I had already seen her a few days post-op as the skin on the reconstruction side was a rather deep purple colour and didn't look particularly healthy. The skin was possibly necrotic (a lack of blood and oxygen to the tissue) and might need removing, but we decided to wait and monitor it until the full results came through. As it happens, this was far from the final picture.

Ms Tait delivered the better news first, which was that the left side was all fine. There was a clear margin around the tumour, and the sentinel nodes, the two lymph nodes that they removed, were clear. However, the right side was 'more complicated', as she put it. There was no clear margin to the skin. When they remove the entire breast and the tumour, they're looking for a margin of tissue all around the tumour to reduce the risk that the cancer might have spread into the tissues beyond. In this instance, the tumour was right on the lower edge of my breast, in the 6-9 o'clock quadrant, and there was no margin between the tumour and my skin. Therefore, the skin had to go too. This would involve removing the implant, cutting the skin away that would have been in contact with the tumour and stitching my chest back up flat. Another body blow.

I started to feel slightly punch-drunk at these consultations. As if I had ridden the crest of one wave and down the other side, only to be buffeted by the next one before I was ready for it, still too preoccupied with how I handled the first.

There was no time to digest this information before the final blow struck.

"Both sentinel nodes on the right-hand side are positive for cancer."

All the lymph nodes had to come out from that side, a full axillary clearance, and I would most likely need chemotherapy. As ever, the news was delivered in a direct but compassionate way. I never quite worked out how she managed it, but Ms Tait had this skill of presenting the information in such a way that you almost knew what was coming, so it took a tiny bit of wind out of the sails. Nevertheless, it was a bitter pill to swallow.

That was a hard day. The hardest, I would say.

When I take myself back there, my memories of that day and the few that followed are indistinct and murky, edged in greyness as if I was looking down a dimly lit tunnel, unclear what else was in there. I could only see what was in front of me, and everything else had faded. The time of year did not help. It was as if I lived in darkness for a while.

The cancer might have spread somewhere else. This was the thing I thought I'd escaped. All the other tests, biopsies and scans showed my lymph nodes to be clear. The reality of the situation was different. My treatment was going to continue for many months to come and include the dreaded chemotherapy I so wanted to avoid. Hidden among that news was the fact that now I no longer had my shiny, new breast implant to mask the truth of losing a breast. I was going to be flat on one side. There was no time to dwell on the implications. There were only four days until this next surgery.

If I had felt a detachment towards my business in the previous eight weeks as this diagnosis has unfolded, now I felt like I could no longer continue. I remember being in tears and feeling quite helpless. How was I going to go through all this and still run a business remotely? I had not been able to set foot in the building since I was shielding, and this would only continue now through chemotherapy. I was not certain I had the strength for it, but neither was I comfortable with the feeling of giving up on something in which I'd invested so much of my energy.

I reached out to my physiotherapy teacher and mentor, Diane Lee, to ask her advice. She kindly arranged a Zoom call with me the following evening. As Diane was based in White Rock, Canada, it was quite late in the UK when we spoke - another memory of the darkness, this time outside my office window while I signed into our call on my laptop.

Diane made it quite simple. As always, direct and to the point, she said the words other people were too frightened to.

"This is about saving your life, Jacqui. Nothing else matters. You can reinvent your work when the time is right. You need to give your team a reason to keep going and for them to take on the lion's share of the responsibility. You need to focus on you."

Saving my life.

Whilst others had skirted around the issue, Diane openly laid it out in full view on the table.

Nothing else matters.

It was a tough conversation, but I welcomed it. I am forever grateful for the directness of her words, sitting as a pivotal moment in my story. It was almost as if they gave me permission to let go of everything else. I needed to hear them. It would take many weeks, if not months, for those words to fully settle within me.

They made their way through my body – from head to brain – searching for a rational explanation. They travelled down the back of my throat, touching lightly on my heart and into my gut where the flame flickered. Instead of burning out, the flame reignited my determination, deep to my root, and my fears spoke to me. I let go, secure in my trust.

The second surgery felt a little bit like returning home; familiar faces on the ward. Ms Tait knew what a tough experience this was for me. Fortunately, I'd managed to squeeze in a hypnotherapy session with Elaine to help me cope with this new reality of what my body was going to look like. I felt calm. I could do this.

There were no tears before this operation. I just wanted to get it over with. On the contrary, there were many s when I came round in recovery! As I emerged from that hazy sleep and gained awareness, the tears started to trickle down my face. The nurse sat with me in recovery, gently holding my arm and allowing me to cry. I didn't feel like I was crying about what happened; it was more of a physical release. I've no idea how long it lasted.

At some point, I was back in my room. Not waiting for any prompts from Nathaniel this time - he'd been given strict instructions to go easy on the 'boob' jokes until I understood how I was going to react to these new circumstances - I had a look. There was my chest with a dressing across it - completely flat.

"There you go, that wasn't so terrible, was it?" the voice in my head reassured me.

After reading posts in the Facebook group of women who have understandably gone days, weeks or even months and been unable to look at themselves, I had vowed to myself not to do that. This was such a deliberate act on my part in search of acceptance.

This is about saving my life.

Following one day in the hospital, I was home to start my post-op recovery - for a second time. I now had numbness under my armpit, down the back of my shoulder blade and greater restriction of movement in my right arm than previously. After making such good progress after the first surgery, it was frustrating to be starting over again.

"Accept it, Jacqui. Get on with changing it."

The return of the diligent patient doing my rehab exercises every day. I turned all sorts of things into rehab tasks. Emptying the dishwasher, trying to put the cups in the higher cupboard, loading the washing machine one item at a time. I measured my success at the point when I could reach the top shelf where the glasses lived or carry a half full basket of wet clothes. As these menial tasks continued, I could see my progression in terms of when my movement increased. I started practicing yoga again.

Prior to the surgery, I bought an online programme where you can access the videos at your leisure. I found it difficult at the time - .my heart wasn't in it, and I was tired all the time. Now, with renewed motivation, I logged back in. I started the daily 15-minute workouts. They were more mobility-based rather than strict yoga poses, so they were perfect for what I was trying to accomplish. For weeks I could hardly do any of it, but I persevered. The first day I could barely do a Child's Pose- there was such limited movement in my shoulder. However, I also knew that if I didn't do something, I would never get the range of movement back. This was one of those times when I really embraced the concept of one tiny step at a time. Do something today. Do something else tomorrow. Then look back over a longer period and see the progress. Don't get attached to how you are doing that day.

Gradually I learnt about this new body of mine. Completely focused on taking the next step.

The beginning of the beginning.

I no longer had cancer - or at least nothing that they were aware of. It was the start of finding my way back to being well again. Yet, it was also the beginning of feeling that I was a cancer-patient. I didn't have any symptoms while I had breast cancer - other than tiredness. Following the surgery, I suddenly had limitations as to what I could do. Knowing that in the coming weeks, this was only going to become more apparent as I moved through to the next phase of my treatment.

Will this tunnel never end? Through the glass, all I can see is my reflection staring back at me from the darkness. The green fields and blue sky that held me in a trance for a few miles are interrupted by the blackness. As the sound of the train on the track rattles in my ears, my eyes fill with unexpected tears which then delicately trickle down my cheeks. Unsettled and embarrassed to look back at my companions, I choose to remain absorbed by my own image. What is happening? Stay calm. It will all be fine once you get there. You'll work something out.

"Heard you were here." My head spins towards the familiar voice and is met by the warm smile of an old friend. "Thought it was you. Are you alright?" Buoyed by her presence, the sadness gradually lifts and we ease into a discussion. She knows me. I have confidence she'll have a good suggestion.

My friend wishes me well before she makes her way back to the doors of the next carriage. Her arrival was an unanticipated but much-welcomed surprise. Our brief conversation even more so. "I'm only in the next coach if you need me," I am reminded.'

5

Unravelling My Identity

"Unravelling external selves and coming home to our real identity is the true meaning of soul work."

— *Sue Monk Kidd, American Writer*

There seemed to be two things that I spent most of October thinking about, according to my journal. One was the impending start of my chemotherapy treatment, scheduled for the beginning of November, and the other was what to do about my business.

The first was made up of meetings with the oncologist, digesting all the reading material they gave me and attempting to dismantle the wall of fear I'd constructed around this event called chemotherapy. I came away from that first encounter with Dr Bradley, the oncologist, and my chemotherapy nurse, Sarah, feeling quite overwhelmed. My thoughts that I'd be all done after surgery and possibly 'back to normal' and back to work by the new year seemed so naïve. Six rounds of treatments, three weeks apart, were proposed, two different types of drugs - known as third-generation chemotherapy. My calendar would be blocked out until late March, with radiotherapy to follow that.

They presented me with all the information, the risks of both proceeding or not with the treatment. It was down to me as an individual to decide how much risk I was prepared to live with. Paul pushed for an answer from Dr Bradley on my level of risk from the cancer. Medium to high was the response.

An average tumour is 15mm; mine was 45mm. Alongside the facts that it was in the lymph nodes, I was relatively young to have cancer, and there were bilateral primary tumours - one in each breast – all put me at a higher risk of recurrence and/or secondary metastasis.

Having a tumour three times the average size swung it for me. To be honest, I had made the decision before I arrived at the appointment. I had absorbed the reality of the cancer spreading beyond the breast, which naturally led to the possibility it could be setting up home elsewhere in my body. I had to throw everything at this. I needed to feel like I had tried everything I could to overcome this.

Chemotherapy is a daunting prospect. I was fortunate that I'd never been through this with anyone close to me. It was rather mystical; something I'd read about or seen on the television. Now it was going to happen to me. Despite those vivid images of gaunt, bald patients sitting in wards with drips in their arms, so many people have it and get through it, one way or another, don't they?

This disquiet was not helped when an acquaintance told me that "I shouldn't have chemotherapy". This was before I knew the full extent of my situation, so I brushed aside the comment with a response along the lines of, "I'll do whatever I think is best". I know they meant well and were concerned about the body-wide impact of chemotherapy drugs. Nevertheless, this made me decidedly angry. It wasn't them looking down the barrel of the gun. I had a reasonable understanding of what chemo was going to do to my body, yet I had to put my trust in the cancer professionals. This is the tool they have. To turn my back on that felt too enormous to contemplate. I placed my trust in my belief that if I looked after myself as well as I could, then my body would bounce back.

I took all the practical steps as advised before the treatment could start. Some simple housekeeping tasks like getting my hair cut, having my flu jab, a visit to the dentist. The gums are one of the areas that can be affected by the treatment, so it was recommended I get a check-up before I start. The chemotherapy placed me as 'extremely clinically vulnerable' in regard to COVID restrictions, so I was going to be pretty limited. This felt peculiar. Earlier in the year, when I had reopened the physio practice to the public, I had been quietly confident that I was not at high risk from the virus. I had happily seen all my returning clients, without undue concern, besides following the government guidelines. This was all to change. The start date loomed large in my calendar - from then onwards, I would be able to do very little. This only served to add to my apprehension. I fell out with Paul about how he was going to have to care for me, hating the thought that I might be dependent. I remember the feeling of the physical, mental and emotional contraction, as my body anticipated that something unpleasant was about to happen. Try as I might, the pull down into this negative vortex was compelling. Each time I peered over its edge, I came back up feeling slightly more troubled but resolved to the fact that it was going to happen regardless.

Distractions were plentiful, on the other hand. A persistent seroma developed in the mastectomy scar that needed draining and dressing on a couple of occasions. My attempts to use K-tape to encourage fluid drainage were unsuccessful but worth a try!

The extent of the restrictions through my right chest and abdomen became increasingly apparent as I struggled to sit upright and could feel the tightness all the way up through the deep cervical fascia into my neck and jawline. I drew my focus towards my routine - meditation, mobility work and my nutrition, anything to feel like I was taking tiny steps forward to getting better, not steps backwards into being a sick patient. Fortuitously, the results of my nutrigenetics test came through just after the second operation. An in-depth call with the nutritionist provided a spotlight for my attention as I started to explore the new eating plan. As such, my days were productively occupied while I hung out in this limbo zone once more.

Following my conversation with Diane, I remained intent on the premise that 'this is about my life, work can be recreated'. It practically became a mantra that I repeated to myself. Though this did not change the fact that I still owned and needed to run a business. I remained unable to physically go into the premises, but I was having regular calls with my practice manager Sarah and check-ins with the therapists. Directly after that conversation with Diane, I arranged a Zoom call to discuss my medical situation where I attempted to give them a reason to take more responsibility rather than just seeing their patients; for them to step up and take ownership of additional tasks. The call was an emotional one for me, coming only days after receiving the news that the cancer had spread. I felt my fingers loosening on the reins, and Sarah was there to take hold of them, but would it be enough? I felt exhausted and vulnerable to be so reliant on these people to sustain the practice. To hope they could care for it as I did. Neither my head nor my heart had space to carry that load anymore.

Letting go was complicated, though. There was so much more than the bricks and mortar of the physical business at stake here. My identity was intertwined and woven within every part of it. Over the previous 13 years of my life, I invested virtually everything I had into it. It grew from scratch - I started with no patients at all, taking over a room in our home with a treatment couch so I could see people when the children were very small. Over the years, as it grew, I took on a shop in the town and another therapist. I thrived as we both flourished with our growing client base. On a day-to-day basis, we made a difference to people's lives. Our reputation spread. People knew who I was, and I took an active role in the town. I met so many wonderful people and made many great friends as a result.

There were plenty of bumps and wrong turns along the road as we continued to expand. I know I made many mistakes; when my passion overflowed, I was often unable to contain it, and it burnt others rather than ignited their own spark within them. I became too accustomed to living so close to the flames to realise. When I was in my clinic room working with my clients, I knew I had a positive impact on their lives. I lost myself in the joy of solving their problems. This was never truer than during the early months of the COVID lockdown. I sat alone in the centre of the fire battling to discover a way to step back through it. I needed to get out. Not many were prepared to reach an arm through to help me. My cancer diagnosis saw me take those first steps directly into the flames.

My journal is littered with entries and comments about how I would cope with work. *How do I do this without it taking everything from me? Can I be detached? Set some boundaries? Do I care? Yes, I do. What can I do? I can do this, or I can do that.* So many conflicting beliefs. Day by day, there was this ongoing dialogue with myself about all the things I could do, but I never questioned what I actually wanted.

Another fateful conversation, this time with a friend who had shut down his own business a year or so before. Similarly, he threw himself into his work with an infectious enthusiasm that lit up all those who crossed his path, including me. I was initially shocked but not surprised when I learnt he was winding up his company. I was aware of the toll it was taking on him, but I believed it meant so much to him that he couldn't possibly stop. He'd put too much into it, surely? However, talking with him that October afternoon, I started to see how all those feelings he described about why he finally called it a day were there for me.

A sense of foreboding hovered over me as we continued to speak. If I couldn't leave work on the back burner, could I create a way of letting go?

"How would it feel if you no longer had to think about the business?" he asked me.

"Lighter. Freer." No hesitation in finding the words. I remember a glimmer of possibility that there might be an alternative to the life I had lived. Right then, I released the notion, dismissing it as not possible. Frightened as to what it might mean.

In the weeks and months to come, I would return to that conversation in my head. Revisiting that feeling of what it might be like not to have the business. I took some tentative steps toward building an exit strategy. Leaning into what had worked before, I considered what I could control and let go of what I could not - enough to be able to stop the chatter in my head. A plan of sorts was emerging, and that gave me some peace of mind. Eventually, in April 2021, shortly before my radiotherapy started, something happened that made my mind up once and for all. I was either selling, closing or giving away the business. This decision unravelled the final few strands of me that were wrapped up in the physio business.

Back in October, though, it was only the first pull of the thread. An acknowledgement that I could change. Actually, that's not true.

I finally started to see that I needed to accept myself as a whole. Not the version of me I thought I needed to be or the one I believed others perceived or needed.

Jacqui - the physio. Jacqui - the business owner and boss. Jacqui - the super-active person who was always on the go. Jacqui - the wife, mother, sister, daughter. Letting go of believing that these labels and roles gave me my worth. Letting go of the belief that I needed to be completely in control of the outcome.

Who was I without all of this? Did I still matter? Did any of it matter now I had cancer? I felt an uncertainty about my future, with dark thoughts about how long I might live. The realisation that the uncertainty had always been there was the lesson yet to be learnt. At this point, I kept coming back to the mantra 'this is about my life, work can be recreated.'

Was it this phenomenon of the layers of my outward persona peeling away what led to my decision to write this book? My mind was certainly more receptive and curious about the world and where I fit into it. I sat in my bubble at home waiting for the next stage in my treatment to happen, looking out at everyone else (well, through the Zoom screen on my computer) living their lives. I became aware of the space that this situation had created, not a feeling I was familiar with or completely at ease with yet.

The idea of the book came to me during an online women's conference I participated in during mid-October. Run by Dr Sam Collins and Aspire, it was a powerful example of all that this new online Zoom-connected world could accomplish. Speakers from the four corners of the globe joined in from their homes to share reinvention ideas. Inspired by the stories of fortitude and struggle and how women can make a difference, no matter how big or small, I wrote in my journal that my action would be to share my story.

My occasional Facebook posts were well received and appeared to resonate with and inspire others. I'd never even considered writing a book on any topic before. Never mind a memoir. Yet this excited me and provided a purpose for my days. I enrolled in an online Women's Writers Circle with a lovely woman called Georgia Varjas, a presenter at the conference. Thankful once more for the lifeline that the pandemic had thrown at me through the explosion of online access to others - with Georgia in Spain and other writers in Quebec and Kenya - I looked forward to our weekly calls. I began to put pen to paper and explore who I was as I started weaving new threads into my identity.

Meanwhile, back in the world, since the children returned to school that autumn, COVID rates were increasing, so there was much debate about a circuit breaker lockdown. Not only was I wrapped up in my own personal health dramas and what my life might look like on the other side of it, but those around me also had their issues. The children did not want to be locked down at home again but we could all see it coming. We were all becoming familiar with the uncertainty and the fact that we were no longer in control of things we normally took for granted. That was about to hit home for us a few days into November.

'I laugh as one of my new companions finishes her tale and notice how easy it feels to be with these strangers who know so little about me. Enjoying each other's company without the need to place them anywhere. I listen and share in return. I forget that we appear to be in the same tunnel. I'm not even sure where we are going anymore. There has been no station for a while. Nothing I can do right now about it. Tired of looking at my reflection in the window I remain engaged in our conversation. That feels better.'

Vignette: Staying on the Path

I stay composed and try not to crumble, coming to terms with the reality of living with a cancer diagnosis. To some, it may appear that I am too positive, trying too hard or even that I am in denial. I am not living a normal life, but then none of us are - we're all living through this pandemic. I am in limbo, treading water as my full diagnosis slowly reveals itself. I choose to believe and trust in myself. Every day I exert razor-sharp focus to keep my thoughts on track, to know that I will find a way and that it is in my power to get through this. This is a battle to be partially fought in my head and amongst my beliefs, not just under the surgeon's knife.

Am I overthinking this? Probably. What else is there to do? I want to be calm, content and enjoy living - whatever that looks like right now. Without this, I am only making myself miserable, and I have to live with that person. Where is the joy in that? I've had depression twice in my life, and I have no intention of allowing myself to go there again. If I am going to choose anything, I'm going to choose which thoughts pass through my head.

I'm looking over the edge as if I am walking on a beautiful yet dramatic clifftop path, like the ones you get in Cornwall, with small craggy bays and waves crashing against the rocks far below. The path is narrow and a few steps away from the cliff face. On those days when I wake up feeling like I cannot continue, it's as if I'm no longer on the path but standing on the brink, right on the edge of that clifftop. I could surrender to my feelings - those dark, enveloping feelings of grief, despair and tremendous sadness. The "why me?" and "it's not fair" where I want to blame someone else, and I hate everyone else for being able to carry on with their lives. I could step over the edge, allow my body to fall into the abyss, and let go of all the pain and hurt. I could stop trying so damn hard every single fucking day to smile and put a brave face on it all. I could relinquish my body to the water, and it would all be over. Abandon my body to the rhythm of the sea, the waves breaking against the rocks. Effectively, surrender myself to the deepest depression I have ever known. And what stops me? Fear. Fear I will never get myself back from that darkness. That I will sink so low, I will never be able to save myself.

That fear guides me from stepping off the cliff. I live with it, embrace it, almost because by not hiding from it, I can invert it into my power. This feels like my superpower now.

On the difficult days, when I contemplate the view from the clifftop, it's tempting to wander dangerously close to the edge, in the knowledge that I don't want to step off, but I don't quite have the energy in that moment, or for that day, to do much more than stare out and wonder.

Some days, I gaze down into the sea and think how bewitching it looks. I call myself back to reality knowing the waves crashing against the rocks appear far more captivating from this viewpoint than being among them.

I take the tiny steps back towards the path. I step off the grassy verge to place my feet firmly onto the worn soil, where so many others have walked before. I turn to face the direction of travel and take the next step forward. I pause and focus on the horizon before I feel strong enough to take another step, but it is enough for that day.

Juniper says ... this t-shirt arrived in the mail a few days after my diagnosis from my friend Nell!

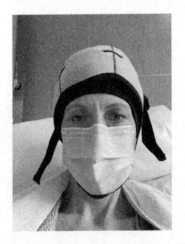

Chemo Cold cap - not the most glamorous photo of wearing the cold cap to try to save my hair during chemo.

Headscarves - the favourite fashion accessory.

Cecilia Costello Photography

Cecelia Costello Photography

My good friend Cecilia did a couple of photo shoots with me to capture some moments from my journey. It was a lovely January day, fortunately, as COVID restrictions wouldn't allow us indoors.

Favourite bald head shot - this was April 2021, so I was pretty used to it by then.

Cecilia Costello Photography

This was the second half of my shoot, not until the July. We both came upon the same idea of the mastectomy scar shots. A number of these went onto be published in *Flourish* magazine produced by the Artlift and Yes to Life cancer charities.

Walk with Jess and Liz - one of many.

Top of Catbells - Paul and me at the summit of Catbells on my anniversary walk.

6

Nobody is Coming to Save Me

"Nobody is coming to save you. You have to learn to save yourself and that starts with getting really honest about where you're at right here right now. Then you work out where you want to be. The gap in-between is the hard work you put in to bridge the gap."

— *Chris Cook, Double Olympian, Speaker & Executive Coach*

Not long after I first shared with someone the way I negotiated my daily walk along the clifftop path, I read this post on social media by my friend, Chris Cook.

Yes! On reading it, I felt strangely liberated.

Nobody is coming to save me from this diagnosis. Not the surgeon, not my husband, not some divine being, no one. I will live with this for the rest of my life. No one else was to blame for me being here. I played my part, I acknowledge this and I take responsibility for it. Now I have to step up to the plate for me. No one else. For me. To keep the spotlight on what matters to me and how I want to handle it. It is time to pull out all the tenacity and resilience I've developed over the years and put it into practice, however hard it seems. I heard someone say once on a podcast that hard work is a choice, not a talent. Why now, of all times, would I choose any other way?

I simply will not give myself the option to sink into that water. I have to save myself. I have to stay on the path.

Following a diagnosis of clinical depression in 2000, I had been on medication for about nine months. It had been tough coping with all the side effects of the drugs and whilst there had been times when they had helped to level my mood, I had felt unsettled for the most part. I was making some significant decisions about my life that would impact my recovery, but there was still this feeling there was something else out there that was magically going to make it all better. That I would wake up and 'feel' differently about myself and my life. Of course, this never happened.

I recall vividly the moment when the realisation hit me that the only person who could change how I felt was me and that I alone could get myself out of this hole. That was the point in 2001 when I decided to come off the antidepressants completely. Reading Chris' words reminded me of that moment. I've done this before, so it is well within my power to find a way now.

This time though, it was a whole new level. Before, I'd felt trapped in a job and stressed by the pressure of it. Now, it was about my life. I told myself *'I am older and wiser. Use that wisdom and make it count.'*

It sounds so simple, written on this page, but it was not easy. Simple solutions rarely are. The gap between where I was and where I wanted to be required quite a feat of engineering to construct a bridge across it. In fairness, this started a few years ago; I didn't arrive there instantly, that's for sure. It was more that the intensity ramped up when the architect let me know about a change of plan - significant progress was required in a condensed timeframe.

I knew I needed to change. Our lives had become unsustainable, and communication had broken down on many levels. Getting the dog, our labradoodle Jess, in 2016 was a major step towards me finding space and peace in my day. She gave the family a focal point for attention and affection, and the kids adored her. It also added some much-needed routine in the day where I had to stop whatever I was doing to take her for a walk. Those walks around the woods were so precious to me and opened up a new world of possibilities. A quiet solitude. However, I didn't have the scaffolding in place to make real progress on the bridge to reach the other side. I was still too busy trying to keep everyone happy rather than looking after myself. The health issues had already started - all of them stress-related. I was living in a cycle of boom and bust as I tried to fit everything in.

I preferred to be doing 'stuff' the majority of the time. The phrase 'if you want something done, give it to the busy person' applied to me for sure! Right now, as I have the space and the silence to reflect and contemplate, I can see how infrequently I was present in my life. I was always thinking about the next thing that had to be done, optimising every task or outing. On the one hand, it is part of who I am and how I've accomplished so many things in my life. However, I was missing the quiet moments between the action.

Planning ahead now meant contemplating the uncertainty of my future. What if the next thing on the agenda is that the cancer comes back? I felt I had to fix everything for everyone else. Living in that place where doing anything for myself would be selfish. I was a mum, a wife, a business owner, a therapist - there were all these other people who 'depended' on me, whom I was 'responsible' for. My whole identity was wrapped up in these roles.

So many of the beliefs I held about how I should live and behave over the years had undermined my agency. I had lost the ability to trust myself and to be me.

I had worked with all sorts of business groups and coaching programmes to find ways to improve my business so that it might better serve my life. There often seemed to be a struggle between what I wanted and what these programmes and people told me 'I should do'. Nothing seemed to fit. I followed the same path over and over again. In December 2017, when I attended my first Aspire Conference, run by Dr Sam Collins, it was as if a veil had been lifted from my eyes.

I found myself in this environment of women who wanted to support each other and believed in themselves. I had spent so much time in a 'man's world' and shied away from women in the workplace after my experiences in both my corporate job at BT and as a physio in the National Health Service (NHS). Yet here were these women shining a light on each other - inspiring and encouraging other women to succeed; to make a difference and change the world. It was phenomenal.

Following her inspirational talk at the conference, I approached the incredible Brita Fernandez-Schmidt to ask if she would become my mentor. Her words had awakened something in me that I wished to explore; they presented an alternative way. Our highly anticipated monthly calls started the ball rolling slowly at first, gathering momentum over the course of the year. Having overcome the inertia at the conference, I committed to myself to take action and there followed quite a few bold steps to change my life - both professional and personal. I made some significant changes at work and started to plan our remarkable family trip to Nepal to track Red Pandas, which we took in April 2019.

The bridge-building had begun. Notwithstanding my brutal honesty about where I was, the self-sabotage continued as I moved across the bridge during construction. My priorities were not terribly different to what they are today, but they were shrouded in a mist of overwhelm, false self-beliefs and assumptions. There was still insufficient self-trust and leadership, I remained drenched in judgement. I could not just be or accept things for what they were. The lack of trust in myself held back the real deep transformation that could be possible. This is, of course, a process, and it would be unfair to say there was no progress. Perhaps it is reasonable to say that for every two steps forward, there was one step back.

In my physiotherapy business, I leased bigger premises in 2018, employed additional staff the following year, and dealt with all the stresses life presented. The missing piece was not truly processing the imprint the stress left on me - both mentally and physically. By now, I was working with some other great business groups, here in the UK, Canada and North America. The lessons I'd learnt through Aspire resulted in better decisions about who I was spending my time with. These groups brought some fantastic people into my orbit, and they would prove to be a lifeline in the looming global crisis.

The pandemic and lockdown forced me to make some long-overdue decisions. I reinvented the business through sheer hard work and persistence. Unfortunately, there remained some deep cuts which bleed over those I loved. I kept battling against those around me. The fall-out of the first lockdown created another tsunami for the family as we were forced to review the kids' schooling and move away from private education. I took it all in my stride, working 12 to 14 hour days in the practice, remodelling the clinical environment to satisfy the stringent COVID procedures to treat people in-person, while simultaneously trying to find new schools. All this with less than half of the pre-pandemic staff, and having worked practically every day since March, without any pay. I was a woman on a mission to fix everything and at the same time, pretended I could keep it up and be present at home.

As the summer unfolded, I started letting go of some of the hurt and anger. The sheer helplessness of the situation and some very wise words, once again from Chris Cook, started to take shape in my brain. By this point, I was sleeping for England on the days I wasn't at the practice for 7.30am. Some very practical things started to fall into place - a sixth form place for Nathaniel at an excellent school, where he could study his music technology; that was paramount. I knew that even though I had made my life harder on the one hand - no staff, a daily commute to take Nathaniel to sixth form - I absolutely trusted these were the right decisions. A weight lifted from me as the anger at the way the previous school had treated us was offset by the removal of such a huge financial burden of school fees. The situation at home started to improve as I was able to be in the house and hold a civil, non-work or school-related conversation. The better weather and easing lockdown restrictions were also helping; there had been a turning point. I felt the tiny flicker of some peace. I could start to think about the jobs at home. I decorated my office. I went on that fateful bike ride.

There is no doubt in my mind that things happen for a reason. The order of events had set our lives up to prepare us for what was about to come.

It could appear I had been dealt another low blow on top of the pandemic events. To me, though, the dealer gave me the cards in the right order. With this knowledge I had the courage to trust I would play a good hand on the days when I needed most.

Each morning, there is a pause at the moment of opening my eyes

- staring out at the world to see how the day might greet me. Will the darkness prevail? Wrapping me in a cloak of sadness all day. I ask myself; *how do I feel?* On certain days, that heavy darkness continues to linger, almost to the point of engulfing me. A physical weight on my shoulders that stops me raising my head from the soft pillow. The thoughts that suck the joy out of the new day before it has even begun. That dread that the depression has arrived. The question of 'will it stay?' drifting through my head. Or will I be able to shake off the slumber to go out and meet the day head-on with vigour and excitement?

The days were always harder when I didn't have somewhere to be by a particular time - where there was less structure to the day. With virtually nothing to do since the diagnosis, it could be insurmountable; I created a structure and framework to hang my day on. I let the routine do all the heavy lifting by reducing the number of decisions to make and the amount of brain energy expended. Taking each step with purpose and on purpose. Paying attention to my actions.

It is funny to think that one of the things we assume creates the disquiet - the Groundhog Day - can be the very thing that absolutely helps us. On the days when I awake to feel brightness and hope, the routine flows with little effort. On others, gradually taking each step at a time brings me close to the cool, calm, blue light. Lightening the load - removing the heaviness from my eyes and the fog from my head.

I had never truly understood the meaning of taking one day at a time. Why would I? I am the planner. The one who knows what I'm doing on a set date and time months ahead. In fact, I know where I was on a date many years ago - holidays, weddings, births - you name them, and I can tell you the date. I carry both my past and future timelines like a giant dragon's tail, lashing from side to side with the scales cutting my skin each time they catch the back of my legs or arms. Like I am reliving each painful moment again as if I hadn't suffered enough the first time. The constant distraction leaving less attention for the moment I was in.

As I write this, I am aware, almost for the first time, that the tail is no longer with me. Or have I managed to find a way to wrap it around me, to carry it without the burden? The feeling is like the tail has transformed into feathers- the wings of a bird - that I can elegantly fold away, under my control. Able to open them out when required for flight, where there is a purpose, otherwise they nestle quietly at my side. I can make them work for me.

I am learning each and every day how to save myself.

'Thoughts pass through my mind about what has happened that day and what is to come. It certainly is not the best day I've ever had, sitting here in coffee-stained clothes, missing half my stuff and running late for the engagement at my end-destination. It is what it is. I will work it out. It was perfectly reasonable to be flustered but now I must keep a calm head, breath and get through the rest of the day, step by step. I'll be on my own once I depart the train, as enjoyable as it is to pass the time listening to new voices. I can cope.'

7

Chemo Interrupted

"You gain strength, courage and confidence by every experience in which you really stop to look fear in the face. You are able to say to yourself, 'I have lived through this horror. I can take the next thing that comes along.' You must do the thing you think you cannot do."

— *Eleanor Roosevelt, American Political Figure, Diplomat & Activist*

"Covid won't kill you, but the cancer might," my oncologist said at my first appointment when asked if he thought my chemotherapy sessions might be affected by the rising COVID infection rates. His words were meant to reassure me that at this point in the pandemic, ensuring continuity of essential cancer treatment was a priority. This eased my worries, but I had not considered the other possibility that managed to blow me off course before we even got that far.

Going for COVID tests has become quite routine for me. I had them before a couple of procedures and both surgeries. I went along to see the nurse for the test, and if I heard nothing, I simply turned up as planned for the procedure - no big deal. I had effectively been shielding since the middle of August with one thing and another, keeping as much distance as I could from my kids when they went back to school. Other than walking Jess and attending hospital visits, I wasn't going anywhere.

Until November. Two days before my chemo was due to start, I went for my COVID test on Monday morning and then carried on about my day. The previous week, the 'circuit breaker' lockdown had begun, but the children were still able to go to school, so it was quiet at home. Paul, in the dining room at work, on Zoom calls or working at the PC, occasionally popping out to get a drink or see how I was. The last couple of weeks had seen my morning routine really come together - cold showers, journaling, meditation and simple yoga Asanas. Along with a hypnotherapy session with Elaine, it was creating a sense of space and calm.

Early on Tuesday morning, I was about to get in the shower when I got a text message from NHS track and trace. I was somewhat confused. 'You have tested positive for COVID…' I didn't finish the rest of the message. I was devastated. Standing by the sink in the bathroom, I fell on my knees. I screamed out 'NO' and burst into angry tears. This was not part of the plan. Everything had been building up to my chemo starting the next day, and now everything has changed. It was a real 'this is not fair' moment. A rather hysterical call to Paul followed to tell him to turn around and collect the children from their various locations. This gave me time to take in what had happened. I couldn't even take Jess out for a walk to cool down before they all got home. So much for my newly cultivated composure. That all went out the window! Everyone else was fed up. Everyone else was bad-tempered. It was not a happy day.

Since I didn't have any symptoms, I fell into full conspiracy theory mode for the rest of the day. The test must be wrong. It's a false positive. As it turned out, me, Nathaniel and his girlfriend, who was staying with us, were positive, and the others came back negative. I did start with symptoms the day after and the nasty cough followed. Nathaniel started with a high temperature later in the week and stayed in bed for a couple of days. No conspiracy then. I had COVID. Most likely, I had picked it up from my hospital procedure to get a portacath fitted ready for my chemotherapy. Quick technical bit again - this is a small disc-like device that they implant just under your skin to give direct access to the subclavicular vein. This protects the vein in the arm from being damaged or collapsing with the repeated injection of the chemo drugs. Oh, the irony of the one person who was shielding in the house catching COVID then giving it to my son, who was in sixth form every day with hundreds of other teenagers.

A friend had recently directed me towards a YouTube video on the Hindsight Window. It's a fun little piece, the crux of which is the effect of shortening the time it takes for you to reflect in a positive fashion on bad events that happen to you. So having gratitude for events in the immediate past gives you faith in the present and the future.

On that miserable Tuesday afternoon in November, as we absorbed the reality of the situation, both Paul and I came to the same positive spin on the situation. If I was going to get COVID, right now was the best possible time it could have happened. Any earlier would have been too close to my surgery; any later and I could have been in the full throes of chemotherapy with a compromised immune system. A great Hindsight Window.

I won't pretend it took away our dissatisfaction that we couldn't leave the house for two weeks. The pressure cooker of isolation would undoubtedly prove a test for the family. There was nowhere to go, but you should avoid being all together - three of us had it and two did not. Having your liberty taken away from you. Feeling responsible for not spreading the virus. I know so many people have shared this peculiar experience during the pandemic. Who would have thought this would ever happen here in the UK?

There was no online shopping booked, so for the first few days, we relied on friends to go shopping and leave it on the doorstep outside until I got more organised. Losing the ability to walk the dog was pretty much the last straw. Jess was alright, though, as there were plenty of offers to walk her. Visitors remained by the gate, and I stood near our doorway to have a short conversation. Standing in our garden with the railings around us felt like we were animals in the zoo.

As my youngest son so beautifully put it on his last evening of isolation as we watched something on the news about coming out of the second national lockdown, "Lockdown is quite easy compared to the last two weeks in proper isolation. It'll feel much easier from now on."

Those two weeks marked a real low point for me as it made me realise how vulnerable I was and how other people exerted a control over my life and well-being that I was most uncomfortable with. I felt ignored by the hospital concerning my delayed chemotherapy. As long as I had COVID nobody appeared to want to know me. There was no conversation about when the chemo might happen or any reassurance about the enforced delay. Multiple negative COVID tests were required before they would allow me to go back into the Yorkshire Clinic. I felt so alone.

There was one conversation with Mandy, my Breast Care Nurse, where I sobbed and sobbed as I told her how I felt everybody had forgotten I had cancer. Yes, I had COVID, but it was just a bit of a cough for me and a distraction from the main event. The fear that had been bubbling up inside me about starting the chemotherapy was really fear about the cancer spreading. At that point, every day further away from starting my treatment became another day when things could get worse. Sharing this fear with Mandy was a relief, and her compassionate response provided the comfort I sought. Allowing myself to feel those feelings helped me to acknowledge the fear and yet accept that I could also live with it. Like opening a pressure valve, the anger was released, leaving me somewhat raw and exposed. The layers I had placed around myself for protection lay discarded on the ground for now. I needed to grant myself the space to be exposed. To unquestionably feel it, all of it, in its most elemental way. Once there was nowhere else for the fear to hide, I could face it head-on.

The following day, the final day of my isolation, was my 49th birthday. After all the other lockdown birthdays in the house in 2020, this was not such a big deal, and a friend's mum did make me the most delicious cake. My other dear friend Alison arrived unexpectedly to see me - through the gate, of course. It was always going to be a strange one as I had expected to spend it recovering from my first chemo session. As it turned out, after Alison's impromptu visit, the cake and listening to our musician friend from the French Alps – Adam, aka Hobo Chic - perform on a Facebook Livestream, it was a lovely day. Lockdown birthdays - another expectation reset.

Besides this, I was buoyed by my upcoming freedom the following day. Jess and I took a very long walk as I relished being out of the house. Another simple moment to cherish and be grateful for. However, a second positive COVID test result the very next day flung me back into conversations with the oncologist and the hospital about a more sensible approach to commencing the treatment. As I repeatedly pointed out to the medical team, other people were not required to have tests to come out of their ten days of isolation and return to work.

"I don't care where I have my treatment now. I've had COVID, so it doesn't need to be green ward," I argued in desperation. Dr Bradley did fight my corner, and eventually, the hospital matron agreed I could start the following week regardless of the result of my next test - which in the end was negative.

Round 1 of chemotherapy was set for the 2nd of December. After all the shock and upset of the COVID episode, the feeling of trepidation gave way to a nervous, almost excited anticipation to start. The admission of how fearful I was about the cancer spreading reignited my courage to meet the challenge head-on. I needed to do this. I could do this. Let's go.

I feel I should point out that this is only my experience of chemotherapy treatment, and I know that others have quite different ones. Anything that I share is in no way meant to be flippant or dismissive, only my recollection of what happened to me.

As I decided to use the cold cap to try to minimise my hair loss, the session would take about 4 hours. I went prepared with flasks of green tea and books to read. I was in a room on my own, and Sarah, my chemo nurse, looked after me very well with a heated blanket to keep me warm as the cap froze my scalp. The weeks of showering my head with cold water paid dividends, coupled with years of skiing holidays sitting on freezing cold chair lifts and open water swimming. The strangest part was removing the cap to find ice on my hair and needing to thaw out before I went home. I had a cracking headache too. Armed with a bagful of anti-sickness medication, I went home and took myself off to a quiet part of the house, away from the smell of the tea being prepared. Chicken fajitas!

Once they had all finished eating and I ventured out of my bedroom, I told Paul, "You'll have to have Chicken fajitas every Wednesday when I've had a treatment. I don't want to get an aversion to more foods and smells than I have to!" It took me many months after the treatment was over before I could even think about eating fajitas again. The mere thought of it brought that sickly feeling to the back of my throat. The same with green tea, well, the particular brand I drank during my actual sessions. I was glad I had restricted what I had to eat and drink, so my stomach did not churn at the thought of more food.

I could best describe the first couple of days as a really bad hangover. The drugs kept the nausea at bay. The worst part was the sensation of blood rushing in my ears, especially at night when I felt that my head might explode. My body didn't quite feel my own; peculiar sensations travelling from head to toe. Nothing specific, but not familiar either. The sense that something was moving through my body. Rather than see it as poison - which it is often referred to as - I chose to see it as a healing fluid finding its way into every little nook and crevice of my body to flush out any rogue cancer cells that might be hiding there. This also helped with the rather alarming, bright red colour of my urine - the nurse did warn me. I tried whatever I could to dampen the fear of now being in this process. Keeping my perspective on the fact that I was moving towards the best opportunity to be free of cancer. Moving forward. Day by day, I felt more like myself. It was a pleasant surprise to feel so much better and be out with Jess again within the week.

Hey, that wasn't so bad, I thought to myself. I chose to focus on being gentle with myself until I started it all over again. To be honest, I enjoyed the time, and space, of having nothing particularly to do and not feeling guilty about it! How great is that?

Consequently, the second round approached with much less worry as I knew what to expect - both bad and good. I could manage the first three hard days with the knowledge that I would emerge again. This one was, in fact, only two days before Christmas. We had made no plans because of the COVID restrictions and the chemo, but I was well enough to go for a walk on Christmas day. In fact, between Christmas and New Year, we had a few family walks planned with friends since we were only able to meet people outdoors. Another expectation reset! I wasn't like a sick person, unable to do anything. If anything, the fresh air, exercise, great company and conversation were the best possible tonic.

The only downside was that on Boxing Day, my hair really began to come out in clumps. A couple of weeks after the first round, I noticed it had started to shed. Sarah did say that it would thin even with the cold cap. However, it felt a whole lot more than thinning. Apart from the awful mess it was making everywhere - hair all over my pillow, the carpet and piles of it in the bottom of the shower, it made me look and feel like an old lady.

"This is not happening to me." I dug a scarf out of the drawer and started messing around with how to tie it into a turban, following a YouTube video. The very next day, I had it all shaved off.

'Suddenly there is a disturbance *"Excuse us please, can we get through? Oh, there you are. We've been looking for you. Here is a drink and a sandwich. Do you need anything else?"* I look up to see two of my fellow commuters from the other carriage cheerfully bustling through. It is terrific to see them; we've shared many a journey along the way. I feel safe, and I remember how well they know me, no explanation required. All those conversations shared over the years as our lives intersected on this route. Thoughtful and considerate, always there when I need them. Polite introductions follow before another passenger asks if they might keep going along the aisle. *"See you soon. You know where we are."* '

Vignette: Who Knew?

Who knew I would look back on my chemotherapy treatment as an empowering experience that freed me from everything I thought I knew about myself. Or even with fondness? I enjoyed the time and space to be gentle and kind to myself. There was a safeness in the structure of the treatment regime that I mourned once it was gone. It was quite tough to readjust to life. That said, some wacky stuff happened that I am glad to be free of.

Before I entered this tunnel, I heard all the stories, a little bit like old wives' tales, about having cancer treatment - the trademark features of what happens to you when you have chemotherapy, like hair loss, for example.

Then there was everything else.

Let's talk about the hair thing first, though. It bothered me way less than I ever could have imagined. The decision to shave my hair off was one of the most liberating choices. Both physically and metaphorically speaking, stripping everything back to nothing and starting again. I loved it. It felt bold. An overriding feeling that I had taken control of what was happening washed over me. Positively uplifting. A 'number 4' was not a haircut that I expected to be asking for, and seeing my hair, or what was left of it, fall to the floor in the salon was odd but not overly upsetting. A few weeks later, as further bald patches appeared, I went the whole hog for a number 1 all over. Watched by my eldest son and his girlfriend, we sat in my kitchen as my friend (and hairdresser) carefully clipped off what little hair was left.

"Well done, Mum. You did well there. I thought you were going to freak out about that." Then, without any more fuss, we moved on with our day.

I was quite fond of my GI Jane look, although initially, I would scare myself on occasions when I caught a glimpse in a mirror. Our hair identifies us to such an extent - long, short, straight, curly, blonde, brunette, grey, natural or highlighted. Having no hair gave me a clean sheet, a blank canvas to be whatever I wanted to be. I did things I would never have done before. Head scarves became accessory number one, and I discovered that you need many of them if you are to coordinate with your wardrobe. I had so many lovely comments from people about the photos I shared online as I took selfie after selfie to record this. In addition, I expanded my collection of woolly hats, generously increased by packages in the post from friends, that kept me warm and stylish over those winter months. I really do not know how bald men aren't wearing a hat all the time in the winter. Even in the house! It gets really cold at times!

I had bought a wig back in October before I was originally due to start chemotherapy. I had a lovely trip to the wig shop in the Leeds' Victorian Quarter with one of my best friends, Claire. Again, not something that I ever thought I would be doing. I told myself not to make too big a deal of it, and Claire brought a light-heartedness to the occasion. Especially when we found out that you couldn't cook with it on as the heat from the oven would melt it. Although I thought I might go for something a bit different, I ended up with a wig as close as damn it to my existing haircut. It's still in the box in the bottom of my wardrobe. I never even thought to take it out.

As the weeks went by during the treatment, hair was disappearing everywhere, and I mean everywhere. Eyebrows, eyelashes, armpits, legs and pubic hair! Yep! It all went. All the hair on my body was gone. Of course, it is obvious when you think about what the chemo is doing; it simply never occurred to me that this would happen.

As I lost my eyelashes and eyebrows, I had to literally paint on my face every day. On a rare occasion when I hadn't bothered, Nathaniel actually asked me to.

"It's freaking me out. Go and put some make-up on. You've got no facial expression with no eyebrows, so I can't tell what you are thinking!"

I developed a new interest in make-up, watching more YouTube videos about drawing on eyebrows and applying false eyelashes. I gave up on the eyelashes pretty quickly as they seemed too much like hard work, but I loved the eyebrows. So many people thought that they were real - even the oncologist made a comment about them when I went for my radiotherapy appointment. Putting my face on formed part of my daily morning ritual, after the meditation and yoga. It wasn't even to face the world; it was purely for me. There were days when it covered up how unwell I looked for sure, and on those occasional days when I felt dreadfully rough, I may not have bothered, but they were few and far between.

Who knew that nasal hair was such a thing? Who knew that losing it would be so much trouble? My nose ran all winter. A steady drip so that the end of my nostrils became sore as I had to keep dabbing my nose. Winter dog walks became a combination of wiping my nose and the tears from my face as the absence of eyelashes led to my eyes watering the majority of the time. My bald head was fine and dandy under my lovely woolly, fleece-lined hat. No problem. The runny nose was so irritating. I'd meet people on my walks and they must have thought I was crying - dabbing my nose and eyes repeatedly. I was like a snotty toddler.

Who knew you turned into a prune? Your skin dries out to the extent that no matter how much water you drink or moisturiser you slather on, it all dries out again in a few hours. On my feet, and towards the end, my hands, the skin began to peel off completely.

My feet burned, throbbed and itched almost from the start, and my hands were either bright red and hot or blanched and freezing - I believe it is a condition known as Palmar-plantar syndrome. Not very pleasant at all. Later on, as I developed more of a peripheral neuropathy, I lost considerable sensation in the tips of my fingers and toes. This has taken a long time to return, and unfortunately, in my hands, it is still diminished. My hands are my tools for my manual work as a physio, so this has been challenging. For so long, there seemed to be nothing coming from them when I first started seeing people again. I am still learning to trust them and know that I can feel what I feel.

Mouth ulcers, bleeding gums, times when everything tastes metallic, of vinegar or of nothing much at all. During those final couple of rounds, when my body did not get on well with the change of drug, my jaw ached so much I could barely chew. I went through the motions of eating because I knew I needed to, really glad I had my eating plan to follow, and my routine bolstered me when I had no energy to think what I needed to nourish me.

Who knew you would wake up one day and feel you had lost all your muscle? It was so strange to reach down one morning to feel these flaccid, fleshy legs in the bed. I could almost get my hand around my thigh! Although I looked great in my yoga leggings it felt so wrong. I've always disliked my legs, especially from the knees up, because they're the chunkiest part of my body, but despite this, I knew it was not good. I had to tell myself this was not a look I should get too attached to. It wasn't going to last and was absolutely and completely bad for my body. The chemotherapy drugs attack the mitochondria in the muscles. Mitochondria are often referred to as the 'powerhouses of the cell' as they produce the energy necessary for the cell's survival and functioning. Consequently, I was quite glad to see them return to something like normal once I could exercise properly again.

It's quite liberating to start again with your hair. As it starts to grow back, you have no idea what it will be. As it turns out, mine was quite dark and sadly greyer than before. I told Paul how upset I'd be if that happened since I was fortunate to have virtually none prior to all of this.

"I don't care if the rest of the female population are embracing their natural grey. I'm not. I'll be getting the bleach out for sure!" I briefly considered going all 1983 and Annie Lennox orange. I went for the full head of bleach instead. Fabulous. I loved it!

Then the hair grows back curly. Google 'chemo and curly hair' - it's a thing. There are loads of posts of women with curly locks that used to be straight. I was uncertain at first, but I have grown to love my curls. No hairdryers, no straighteners - just some gel, a quick scrunch and I'm done. Don't tell anyone, but I've even thought about getting it shaved off again - maybe not quite a number one again. But you never know?

What was not so much fun was losing my fingernails. During the treatment, they started to develop ridges and gradually became more discoloured. I wore dark nail polish most of the time to cover it up. Once they started to grow properly, they began to lift and eventually fall off, leaving me with a bare, exposed nail bed. I recorded the event in my journal on what felt like a day-by-day basis - 'oops, there goes another one!' Boy was it sore though. Coupled with the numbness I had in my fingers from the peripheral neuropathy, I was horribly clumsy and useless. I couldn't open tins, cans or jars, clip open my make-up, or fasten buttons.

The wonder of the human body meant that I could see myself repairing - my hair and nails regrowing, the skin rehydrating, the sensation slowly returning to my hands and feet. Nothing is quite how it was, but then that is true of so much more than my physical body. Through all that loss, I have learned to appreciate what my body is and does for me. That if I take care of it, it will give back to me a living, breathing container within which I can live the life I choose. To lose so many pieces of myself in such a short space of time was frightening, never quite sure what would be undone or not. One thing is for certain, I will never take this body of mine and what it can do for granted ever again.

8

As the Waves Come Crashing In

"You may encounter many defeats, but you must not be defeated. In fact, it may be necessary to encounter the defeats, so you can know who you are, what you can rise from, how you can still come out of it."

— *Maya Angelou, American Memoirist*

"So how are you?" a friend asked me after my surgeries back in October 2020.

"I'm doing well, thanks," I replied.

"No, how are you REALLY? Not what you are telling everyone else," she continued.

"Really, I am well. I genuinely feel positive. It's not an act."

There have been so many times when I have asked myself whether I was in denial and if all the positivity was put on to make me feel better and for others to think I was being strong. The answer was always the same. I actually did feel great in myself the majority of the time. Even as the chemo sessions started to take their toll, I bounced back after a few days, almost forgetting how terribly I'd felt only a few days before.

When I hit February and chemo round number 4, my perceptions began to shift. I didn't get on well with the change of chemotherapy drug - Docetaxel - and the altered protocol. Instead of taking the steroids intravenously at the start of the treatment session, I took them orally for three days - starting the day before. Rather than my fatigued and hungover state on treatment day and the day after, I was like Tigger - full of life, bouncing around with sufficient energy to carry on like nothing was happening. Then on day three, I crashed. On Saturday morning, I literally couldn't move. Every joint in my body ached, and I could barely get out of bed and onto the sofa. The fatigue was like nothing I had ever experienced. We'd planned to watch the first weekend of the Six Nations Rugby that day, so I was literally sprawled on the sofa all day. I slept through most of the match, mind you - not such a bad thing as we lost to Scotland at Twickenham for the first time in goodness knows how many years!

I knew that the aching would be better if I could move, so the next day, I went out for a short dog walk with Nathaniel. So often, I heard the voice in my head reminding me that fatigue would be eased by keeping a level of activity going. The less I do, the less I'll be able to do. It requires the reasoned evaluation of what is enough and not too much. This was not about pushing myself when I needed to be kind. However, at times it required gentle encouragement to get going.

During that weekend, I developed symptoms that would go on to plague me in some form or other for weeks to come. I will refrain from sharing all the details, not least because it is a bit personal, and I doubt you would want to read it. Essentially, I was itching - everywhere! Every orifice and crevice - my mouth, nostrils, eyes, armpits, groin and a few that I will leave out, but I'm sure you get the general idea - had some kind of itchy rash.

The medical team had stressed the importance of contacting them if I had any issues or felt unwell. With a compromised immune system, there was always the risk of getting an infection that my body may not be able to fight off. This has always been the case, of course, for cancer patients - avoiding others with coughs and colds. With COVID looming over all our lives, this could easily be forgotten. Eventually, by Monday morning, Paul said that I must call someone. I was stuck in 'I don't want to bother them. It's probably nothing' mode. It was, of course, the right thing to do.

Once I'd spoken to the nurse and the oncologist, I went to see the GP, who diagnosed thrush - of one form or another. Oh joy! I left with about four different potions and lotions, and fortunately, over the next couple of days, the symptoms eased. There was a good ten days of feeling better before I went again. Armed with various drugs to take prophylactically, I was semi-confident I could handle it again. More trepidation accompanied me on the way to the clinic for the fifth round. The expectation of knowing what was to come was so much harder to deal with this time around, and Sarah's reassurance that lots of people find this drug harder was little consolation. Now I was finding out how tough this can be.

Unsurprisingly, I went around the same cycle of boom then bust. In full Tigger mode, I talked myself into believing that it wasn't going to beat me again and I wasn't going to crash. Then on day three, I awoke, once again, more like Eeyore than Tigger - listless and low. More skin rashes on my hands and face this time, befriended the thrush invasion from before. My cheeks were burning hot, raw and red, and none of the creams made a difference.

In the end, it was Alison who once again rode to my rescue, driving the 20 or so miles from her house to bring me something to try. She admitted that it gave her a good excuse to get out of the house.

It was March 2021, and we were still in a tight lockdown, so any valid reason to excuse yourself from the pressure cooker of home was a bonus.

Despondent. Uncomfortable. Fearful. Feelings that I had kept at bay were breaking on the shore now. The loss of sensation in my hands and feet worsened. I felt that I was losing my grip. Only one more round to go. Then this will all be done. I will have made it through to the end. Survived. A real warrior.

The days ticked by with little respite and no real feeling of wellness or recovery as previously. On those days when I felt about 90, and every joint in my body hurt, and all these annoying little things were happening to me, it is so hard not to lose faith and break down. Or feel helpless. For the most part, I surrendered myself to the fact that I couldn't do anything and had to sit and rest. For me to be strong enough to let go of my 'plan' for that time was quite something. Especially when I didn't beat myself up about everything I meant to do that day, it is the ultimate test in living in the moment and caring for yourself.

During those days, I flicked between vegging on the sofa, watching endless episodes of French TV, pottering around the house or walking Jess as I felt able. If I wanted to, I approached a bit of writing if I needed to think - but not to satisfy some deadline, simply because it felt like the right thing to do. There was no guilt about not doing things. In the past, whenever I was ill, I always worried about what was not getting done. What changed? I think the space and silence I created in the run-up to this time meant that I grew comfortable with just being. No judgement. No guilt. Just being how I needed to be right then. I am not a lazy person. I never could be. I will always tackle the next 'job' to be done. I didn't hold the belief that I became a lazy person. I learnt the beauty of 'being more, doing less'.

If people asked how I was, I would tell them honestly, "I'm rough. I feel rubbish". I knew that it would pass. I tried not to get upset about the treatment. I embarked on it knowing it was going to be horrid. No one can prepare you for it. Losing your hair, eyebrows, lashes. All the odd sensations of burning, itchy skin, feeling like a prune, a permanently running nose. Not being able to eat as your jaw aches and your mouth has lots of sores and food tastes of nothing, and you keep burning your mouth as you've lost sensation. Numb, sore fingertips each time you touch things. A paper cut that doesn't heal.

The poison of chemo mops up any rogue cancer cells that may be there. It is a means to a very important end. You don't have to be too stoic and pretend that it wasn't horrid. It was. I feel so fortunate it took that long to get this bad. However, the body is an amazing thing, and constantly works to repair itself, so during the days between the rounds, things improved. That is what I remembered on those days when it was all too awful to contemplate. I am so close. My body will recover. And my mind.

I had conversations with Dr Bradley about whether I should continue as he was concerned about neuropathy. Another round would almost certainly make it worse, and the differential between five and six rounds of chemo turns out to be negligible. I got a real sense that the approach is they throw as much treatment at you until you hold up a white flag and say no more. I did not want to be defeated. Even then, after all, that had happened, the achiever in me still felt that to fall at this last hurdle would be failure. I turned up on the Monday as planned for my COVID tests and bloods. However, talking with Sarah made me recognise that I had to let go. I wept in her office as we made the decision to go no further.

"You've made it all this way with barely a word or a tear. It's okay to stop. You've done enough." Too exhausted from the last three weeks to keep fighting, I waved the flag.

What a strange anti-climax that day was. Rather than feeling elated that it was over, I felt flat. I had no idea what I should have felt like. This date had been in my mind for four months, and now it had arrived, I was lost. Worse was to come. After priding myself on getting out of bed every day - reasonably bright and early - staying on the path and wanting to engage in my routine, I stumbled and fell off the edge.

Vignette: Clinging On

I have no desire to get up, so instead pretend it's my choice to stay in bed to read and drink my tea. Some days this might feel good, but then I find myself staring out of the bedroom window, and the tears start to trickle down my cheeks. The feeling of not wanting to do anything washes over me like the waves crashing against the rocks. It is not something I can control, and almost no matter what I do, I cannot shake it. I manage to scramble a little way off the rocks and start to climb back up the cliff face, but I am not able to hold on well enough. There is not enough strength in me to keep pulling myself back up - my poor, sore fingers that have no feeling in the tips right now simply cannot find the purchase on the rocks to allow me to pull my body higher. I lose my grip and slide back down again.

Right now, I don't know how long this will last. I have lost ground on all that work I have done, and my head is no longer quiet - the train of thoughts and words are with me, demanding I give my attention to them and what they represent. I check myself when I give in to the urge to let my mind go with all the chatter - but it is hard. I find myself revisiting my journal and notes where I have captured all that positivity and discovery of who I am - unmasking the person I now wish to be. I have faith I can make it back up to the path at the top of the cliff. I know where I want to be and how I want to feel. I'm finding alternate days of good and bad.

I look for reasons. Evidently, this is very common - people are often worse a week or so after they finish their chemotherapy and/or radiotherapy. It's all done, but you do not feel any better. Whilst this may be true, knowing that doesn't really help me to deal with it.

I have approached all this with the attitude that I wouldn't be held to convention. I want and I will be one of those who can smile and see the silver lining in every cloud - the cancer, the COVID, the changing schools, the lockdown - I have found a reason why all of these things are leaving me and my family in a better position than when we started.

All I know right now is that the emotion needs to come out for me to heal. My body needs to recover, so it wants me to slow down. My desire is to balance that with doing the right things for my body as I have followed the nutrition and done my exercise all the way through this, knowing that my body will be better for moving. I am fighting to keep that spirit and not succumb to the temptation of letting the waves wash me out to sea. I must keep hold of the rocks. This is like nothing I've ever experienced before. I have only tears.

9

Penultimate Stop

"There we both sat and rested for a while, facing the rising sun the way we'd climbed, for looking back can sometimes help you on."

- *Dante, Italian Poet, Writer & Philosopher*

The final leg of the journey. Radiotherapy treatment is like that extra scene in a movie that's partway through the end credits or even annoyingly right at the very end - you'll get this if you've ever seen a Marvel movie! It's supposed to be relatively straightforward, particularly if you've already had chemo, according to the oncologist. I met her at my first visit to the Bexley Wing at St James' Hospital in Leeds, the large specialist cancer unit we're fortunate enough to have nearby.

"Most women like you who've already had chemotherapy find radiation quite straightforward and not as tiring."

Sounded good to me.

What sounded less appealing was the list of possible risks associated with the radiation, including lung damage and a high-grade, difficult-to-treat sarcoma. Nevertheless, the risk of recurrence from my breast cancer was still higher, so I smiled, signed the paperwork and agreed to proceed. Similar to the decision about embarking on chemotherapy it's a roll of the dice.

My experience of radiotherapy turned out to be rather profound. One of being so within myself that it was a meditative experience. My memory of that time is of me alone in that room. I have limited recollection of anyone that I interacted with. On the other hand, it did not meet my expectation of being easy compared to chemotherapy - it was extremely tiring. You win some, you lose some, I guess. Luckily, I only had to attend five times for treatment. The surgeon and oncologist had decided I was appropriate for a new protocol, to receive a higher dose of radiation over five visits rather than the usual fifteen.

After the winter of a COVID lockdown and my chemotherapy treatment, I hadn't been anywhere. Therefore, the prospect of getting in the car and driving to Leeds held some appeal. I got dressed up. It was an opportunity to wear my smarter clothes, with a matching head scarf, of course. Having arranged for several friends to give me a lift there, .it turned into an exciting social engagement!

Paul took me for the initial preparatory visit though. When I arrived at the large unit for the first time, being around so many people verged on the peculiar. My days were so often spent alone in the house with my dog. I hadn't been to a supermarket since early November. There were visits for my chemotherapy, and a couple of appointments with the local GP of course, but outside my immediate family, groups of people were few and far between.

And all these people had a story. Like me, they all had cancer of one kind or another. Most were on their own as they waited for the lift, queued for reception, or sat, wearing their masks, apart from each other in the waiting area. It was a strange experience to feel part of a community yet utterly alone at the same time. One lady spoke to me about three or four days into my visits which I found curiously difficult to handle. I hadn't really spoken to any other cancer patients as in most of the environments I'd found myself in, it felt like quite an imposition to strike up a casual conversation. We were all like small islands sharing a common ocean with no apparent need to be closer to each other. There was a transience to the experience. Yet she was keen to share her wisdom with me about what she found helpful in her recovery. I smiled politely, made eye contact above my mask, despite my awkwardness, and listened calmly to her words.

The first visit was a couple of weeks before the treatment started. This involved a 'setup' exercise whereby they could measure and record exactly how you were to lie, so the correct and identical areas were radiated at each treatment session. They tattooed a few dots on your skin to act as markers in order to replicate the alignment every time. Initially, it hadn't made a huge amount of sense to me, if I'm honest; it became clearer, though, once I was in the room.

They explained to me that because of the area being treated, I needed to do some breath-holding to inflate the lungs so the heart was moved slightly out of the way to reduce the risk of damaging it. Unfortunately, there is often a chance that the lungs themselves can be scarred. Roll the dice.

Fortunately, a fellow friend and physio, who had breast cancer a few years before, had told me about the breath-holding already, so I was prepared. The radiographer demonstrated how I should breathe in for a count of 6, hold for up to 25 seconds and repeat 3 to 4 times for each side. I was having radiation both on my left breast after the lumpectomy and on my mastectomy scar and right chest wall. I'm not certain how common it is to radiate mastectomy scars; however, my understanding was that because of the risk that the cancer might have spread to the skin they wanted to be doubly sure they got anything the surgery might've missed.

When I was called through to the treatment room to see the two radiographers setting up my treatment, I was asked to remove my clothing to the waist and lie naked on the hard bed. My arms were placed above my head, resting in a support and holding on to a bar while they took lots of measurements to record exactly how I was positioned. They watched from their room as I held my breath to make sure I could repeat it precisely the same every time and they could see exactly the same part of me.

"That's really good. I've never seen anyone breathe in that evenly and consistently each time," the radiographer informed me through the microphone. I chuckled to myself, thankful that all those hours of pranayama - breathwork - practice each morning unexpectedly proved so useful.

The tattoos were something of a disappointment, though. Two tiny dots on my sternum and one in each armpit, barely visible unless you looked hard. I had the impression from speaking to a couple of other people that they might be a bit more significant.

All of this took time. I was cold, and my arms were terribly sore. I often got pins and needles in my right forearm and hand if it was elevated above my head, and all the back of the arm, armpit and shoulder blade remained numb. This would not be a position of choice! I kept thinking, *how on earth can other people do this if they're older and less mobile or haven't got movement back in their arms after the surgery?* I had worked tirelessly to restore my range of movement, particularly on my right side - I'd seen too many stiff, immobile frozen shoulders in my time, so I had consistently shown up each day to work through the self-prescribed rehab regime. Not everyone would have been able to do that, so this must be so difficult for them. Aside from the discomfort, it was emotionally demanding to lay there, stripped off to the waist with my one remaining breast on show and my mastectomy scar on full view to these two women.

They do this all day, every day. You know what it is like to look at people's bodies all day but not really see them. They are not thinking anything about you or how you look. It's their job. They are extremely professional. And they absolutely were. There was no question about how anyone behaved towards me: considerate, polite, clear, specific instructions and extremely sensitive handling if any was required. It was more that I felt like a body, a specimen, rather than a person. Goodness knows I was probably the tenth person they'd seen that day. They had a very important task that required the utmost accuracy from what I could make out from their exchange on the measurements they were taking. They didn't have time for small talk or to ask me how my day was going. Get over yourself, Jacqui!

In the intervening time, there was another significant turning point. I made the definite decision that I would sell my physio business. During all those months since my conversations with Diane and Chris, which sowed the seed of extracting myself, various discussions had been taking place about possible exit strategies, but with little tangible progress. When the final straw broke the camel's back, I was under no doubt that I wanted to get out completely, and in as short a timeframe as realistically possible. This was another of those weightless moments. The feeling of freedom at the possibility of how my life might be. The combination of the knowledge that I was nearing the end of my treatment and the catalyst for making the decision seemed perfectly timed. I had been building up to this.

It was sunny during my treatment week. I remember that vividly as the late spring unfolded. After an hour each way in the car and an hour or two at the hospital, by the time I returned home, I sat in the garden or perhaps in our living room and slept. I was unquestionably tired. My expectation that my heroic journey through chemotherapy, feeling so surprisingly well for so much of it, was going to carry me through this experience proved unfounded. I had no choice but to surrender to my body's need to rest. I went through the process without ever specifically looking into what the radiation was doing to my body. The oncologist had mentioned that the side effects might continue and could peak around two weeks after I completed the sessions. Paul had done some research, but when questioned, he responded, "I'm not sure that you want to know while you're going through it. Maybe we can talk about it when you have finished." Fair enough! I let it go. Sometimes ignorance is better. On the upside, my skin did not burn, which I was grateful for, having seen photographs of what other women had experienced.

The fatigue did last for a few weeks, as expected, but this was the last hurdle I had to face in terms of treatment. I had already started the hormone therapy I will be on for the next 5 to 10 years to reduce the amount of oestrogen my body produces in the hope no further oestrogen-fed tumours can develop. At this point in my journey, I felt like I was so near the end. I know now, as I live with the long-term medication, that the journey hasn't finished. That was just one stop along the way. Although the ending of it did signify a break in the regular toing and froing to hospital appointments.

Rather fittingly, I had organised for Paul and I to go away for the weekend back to the Lake District the day after my treatment finished. Back to the same B&B we stayed at for those couple of days after my diagnosis. Returning to the place which has proven to be a gentle oasis of calm in those initial turbulent few days. We were blessed with sunny weather, and I managed to do a couple of quite decent walks. It proved to be a perfect interlude to the story. It felt as if I could turn my attention now to what came next, even though I had no real idea what I wanted that to be.

'Wow! This feels like a long journey. Leaving the station this morning seems like an age ago. My mood has settled, like a pebble on a beach, gently rolling with the tide, in and out, but content to be where it ends up. I rub my eyes to adjust to the light, bringing more awareness to my surroundings after my short nap. Finally! We've reached the end of that dark tunnel and the new landscape reveals itself. The carriage has more of a buzz about it; we must be approaching a stop because people are collecting their luggage off the racks. The seats around me are occupied by new faces. I must have missed others leaving the train while I slept. This isn't my stop, though. A little bit further to go.

I peer out of the window. Nearly there. I wonder if I should get up now, collect my bags, and wait closer to the door. A fellow passenger at my table gestures toward me and says, "What's the rush? There will be plenty of time once the guard announces the upcoming destination. Enjoy the last part of the journey. You'll have enough to think about when you get off. Make the most of these last few minutes." I shrug my shoulders in agreement and settle back. No panic. Remember to find the space. All the other stuff is going to happen regardless. Just 'be' for a while longer.'

Vignette: Alone with my Breath

"Silence, I discover, is something you can actually hear."

— *Haruki Murakami, Kafka on the Shore*

Inhale, exhale. Inhale, exhale. My eyes focus on the ceiling above me, my mind stays in my body, I block out the sounds of the machines angled around my chest. I am not thinking about what they are doing to me. This is the last step of the journey. Stay focused.

Everything is white, clinical and clean. There are no windows anywhere. It all feels efficient, organised, and productive, but this only lends to the sensation that I am on a conveyor belt. Radiotherapy treatment looks as if it is about moving the bodies through expensive equipment in as timely a fashion as possible. The staff are all friendly and attentive, but I never really get to know anyone. They never really get to know me. Each day when I arrive, I meet a different group of people.

I understand why it is this way. I only ask to be treated as a human being, and I am. There's just something missing. A connection?

I change into the hospital gown, stripped naked to the waist, and lie on the bed. On my back with my head in the hard frame, they ask me to open the gown. I interlace my fingers and place my hands on a bar above my head, ready to keep them there for the whole session. They move me around in a gentle, respectful way as they manoeuvre the various bits of equipment around. They keep checking and rechecking to see that I am in exactly the right place.

Lots of people have seen my body by now. It doesn't bother you.

Then again, it sort of does. I know they don't really see the bodies; they see through different eyes. That doesn't remove the feeling of vulnerability.

After the first session, when I was so cold lying on the bed, I turn up today with my bed socks, thicker jogging bottoms and a thin skullcap for my bald head. I joke that I should've brought my teddy bear. I climb onto the treatment couch and arrange myself, wrapping the blanket from the waist down and around my legs and feet. There's nothing I can do to keep the top of my body warm. That was perhaps a glimmer of a smile or acknowledgement from the team, but they're very focused on getting the job done. They're all terribly polite, courteous and considerate. I am seeking that flicker of warmth to be seen by them.

They introduce themselves. Desperate for a human connection in the space-age room, I want to ask one of them what they did last night. The day when I see the same person from two days ago, I wish I had something to say to them for the recognition that we've met before. Maybe it's because I don't want to be forgettable. Simply another person who passed through. That feeling again of merely being a statistic. I feel no judgement or criticism of these professionals as they go about their day, but this whole experience has felt like I was slightly invisible. In soft focus, I move around this large building, take my place in the queue and then leave no impression on anyone there. As I near the end of this treatment journey, I want to feel like it's mattered. Like I have mattered. Will someone along the way remember having spent time with me? Just as I look back over the years and remember patients I've seen. Not the ones who have become good friends but the ones I only knew briefly, but there was something about them, something they said or did that means I remember when our paths crossed.

Back in that dimly lit room with my vision restricted to one point above me, there is a screen above my head running through a random selection of photographs of the local area; a distraction once everyone else has left the room and I am alone. One final check before they leave, a long pause before I hear the voice on the intercom. For the first four sessions, I am convinced they are closer, just behind what I thought was a window in the right-hand corner of the room. When I look to see it, there is no window in the corner of the room; just a mirror. They are in a room way down the corridor - further testament to the fact nobody wants to be in the room or anywhere near when the radiation is switched on. I let that thought go.

'Breathe in, hold your breath………. let it go,' I follow the instructions. I go inward to where I take myself in my morning meditations. I am grateful for my breath work. The pranayama techniques I practice regularly feel as if they've all led me to this point. I can cope with this stressful situation. I can comfortably breathe in for a count of six and hold my breath for a count of 25. I understand how important it is to completely breathe out in order that I can breathe in again. At moments I'm able to lose myself whilst in the background I am breathing in, holding then breathing out. No panic or fear that 25 seconds feels too long. I feel comfortable, relaxed and grateful that I discovered the power of my breath.

The power to think and be still. The power to not rush or fidget. I laugh to myself one day when only moments after the staff leave the room, I feel an itch on the back of my neck that I cannot scratch; one movement and they would have to start the whole set-up again. I bring to mind the sole focus of my breath and draw attention away from that sensation; the desire to tend to that feeling ebbs away. An internal smile, it feels that I've been preparing for this moment for months.

My mind does wander at times to the photographs flashing above me on the screen, a supposed random selection of photographs of Yorkshire taken by patients. My brain wrestles with frustration because the same pictures keep coming up, telling me they're not random. Let it go. Breathe.

I am grateful to feel my breath. I am grateful to have built a relationship with my breath that means I am no longer afraid of it. That I can allow it to rise and fall, watch it when I need to, or use it to serve me, my body and my mind. Alone in the room. Alone with my breath.

Vignette: Has it Worked?

Did the treatment work?

Have you been given the all-clear?

Are you in remission?

Has all the cancer gone?

Are you cured?

I don't have answers to these questions. Or at least not answers that will give the comfort they seek.

As I step back into the world, those I meet enquire about my well-being and then often ask one of these questions.

I start off by responding with explanations about how the treatment works - the risks and unknowns. Some people get it, many do not. They want a simple answer. It is easier.

I live in the knowledge I have done everything that I could to give myself the best chance of no recurrence. Beyond that, I can't think about it. I will drive myself insane.

I find a place of calm, peace and contentment each day so that if such thoughts arise, I can manage that uncertainty and live with it.

I have no energy to spare to explain again.

Next time, I say, 'Yes. I am fine, thank you.'

The (Wo)Man in the Arena

"It is not the critic who counts; not the man who points out how the strong man stumbles, or where the doer of deeds could have done them better. The credit belongs to the man who is actually in the arena, whose face is marred by dust and sweat and blood; who strives valiantly; who errs, who comes short again and again, because there is no effort without error and shortcoming; but who does actually strive to do the deeds; who knows great enthusiasms, the great devotions; who spends himself in a worthy cause; who at the best knows in the end the triumph of high achievement, and who at the worst, if he fails, at least fails while daring greatly, so that his place shall never be with those cold and timid souls who neither know victory nor defeat."

— *Theodore Roosevelt, former US President*

'The Man in the Arena' by former US president, Theodore Roosevelt, is a quote from a speech he gave in 1910 called 'Citizenship In a Republic' at the Sorbonne in Paris, a year after leaving office.

10

Destination Anywhere…

"One's destination is never a place, but a new way of seeing things."

— Henry Miller, American Novelist

Sudden. That is how it felt to reach the end of my radiotherapy treatment and be 'finished'. I left the Bexley wing that day to no fanfare or applause. As with the end of the chemo treatment, this felt such an anti-climax. I have no idea what I expected to happen. After all those months of having the treatment structure laid out ahead, it was all gone. I had reached the end.

The thing was, I never chose to buy the ticket that got me here, so I had no idea where I actually was. It was disorientating as I attempted to work it out. Arriving at this point in the story was when the analogy of the train platform came to me. As I wrote about how I felt to be finished, I found myself considering what to do next as if I had arrived in a new city or country. What would I do? How would I explore the location? What might I see there? I love the parallel with travelling - where you accept to let yourself be surprised by the people, the culture and the places you find once you get there rather than planning every little detail.

On the other hand, this place didn't need to be my journey's end. At any point, I could purchase another ticket to go somewhere else of my choosing. This was reassuring and prevented me from feeling trapped at a dead-end. I had the power to seek out another place given the space to decide where. Perhaps I needed to look at a few travel books to see what I fancied? Then again, I didn't have to walk the same path as those before me. This is my journey for me to sculpt in any way that suits my unique personality. I needed to be curious and receptive to the world around me. More inquisitive about all the possibilities. It was exhilarating and unsettling in equal measure.

Amid this, I returned to work one day a week. One of my physios had decided to leave so I needed to pick up the overflow of patients. This was hard since I was neither physically nor mentally ready. However, it got me back out into the world and helped to cement the decision that I was ready to move on. I saw so clearly that I was not the same. That life was not the same. Wherever I'd been before was not where I was now. This environment was not bringing me much joy.

As crazy as it sounds, during all this time I remained engaged in learning. I'd taken various online coaching courses since my diagnosis; these proved a lifeline for me in numerous ways. I kept in touch with a wider community, could utilise my brain and pursue a line of self-inquiry to scrutinise my personal and professional desires. These people outside of my direct sphere offered a more objective perspective. As I came to the end of the radiotherapy, right when I was standing on the station platform looking around without a clue what to do, one of these courses proved to be instrumental in helping me craft what I might explore next. Or at least what I wanted to get closer to and how I might start on a path to get there, providing the clarity that selling the business was the right next step. That feeling of freedom, weightlessness and relief was strong. Sensing this deep, deep within my core meant I never questioned the decision.

I had the first place to visit and a focus for my attention. Yes, absolutely, it was a distraction from addressing other feelings of uncertainty and being uncomfortable, but I could only move forward one step at a time as I allowed the mud to settle and for the water to clear. This was the right place to go.

'I'm here. My destination. Time to collect what is left of my belongings and leave the train. I say my goodbyes to those I have shared the journey with, expressing a desire to meet again. I thank them for their support and openness for giving a seat to what must have seemed like a slightly crazy woman covered in coffee stains clutching her possessions. I express my gratitude that they made light of it and made me feel so welcome and comfortable. I look around to see if anyone I know is still in the other carriage, but it is busier there now and I cannot recognise anyone. No time to linger. I make my way hurriedly down the train steps. Just like that, I am on the platform. As abruptly as the train halted earlier on, my journey is over. Standing alone, in the fresh air feeling exposed and unsure.

Where am I? The surroundings feel strangely obscure, yet it is the right place. Something has changed from a previous visit. I pause to recall what I had decided to do to rectify the day. Too late for my appointment, I need to explore an alternative way to spend my time.

Right, I know what I will do. I take one last look at the train disappearing down the track before I turn to the exit of the station. I'm quite excited to see what's going to be outside the door. This feels like unknown territory for me, but I need to explore this place. Maybe not be for long, but this is where I am now. Let's see what there is to find and enjoy the experience.'

Emerging with power

I start the exploration of recovery.

All I have experienced stripped me to my bare bones. Yet I'm not trying to return to something. Rather I am learning to live with the new, in body and mind.

Having the rug pulled from under my feet as the discovery of the cancer stopped everything.

Treading water, waiting for the full diagnosis. Exposed and vulnerable.

Next, the process of taking everything away to allow what was already there to rise to the surface:

the surgery, like a strange, new beginning.

the chemotherapy, when at times I was so unwell it was as if they ripped my guts out and left them on the ground right in front of me.

the radiotherapy; like a weird glitch in *The Matrix* where I was exposed and so alone, so focused, so measured, so controlled.

Deciding to sell the business - the last vestige of who I was before - I could start to rebuild who I am now.

Not who I'm going to be. I don't know who I'm going to be. I just know who I am now.

As I emerge from the flames, everything else has burnt away, I come out stronger, revitalised and renewed.

It's a little uncomfortable at times negotiating where I am. I ended up in a place where arguably, I have everything I thought I wanted.

Yet it still does not feel quite right?

I take myself back to those days during treatment and say to myself, 'live day by day right now.'

I am not replacing the labels and roles of old with new ones - the cancer patient, the cancer survivor, the yoga teacher, the writer, the coach - all more badges to stick on my chest that hide the whole me.

I am all those things, yes, yet so much more. The outside world needs to see those titles to place me somewhere in the frame.

When I need them to know who I am I have lost my way.

When I struggle with where I am, I sit with that feeling and let it settle.

I return to the moment of acceptance. That deep knowing and trust in myself that I can live with the uncertainty and the fear.

Whenever I accept myself with no judgement, I spread my wings a little further, raise my head a little higher, shine a little brighter.

I rise to my power and all that I am.

11

Loving My Battle Scars

*"Make peace with your body today, my friend, say your
apologies, right your wrongs and move on with
appreciation."*

— *Donna Ashworth, Poet*

Our bodies tell a story, of that there is no doubt. The physical
changes to my body as a result of now living in Cancer Land could
possibly be one of the hardest things to live with. Oddly, the
presence of a 9" scar across my chest where my right breast used
to be did not have the impact I expected.

The scars on our bodies all tell a story or act as a reminder of what
has happened to us - what caused the lasting mark. As my scar
count increased over the recent months, I have taken each one and
assimilated it into my being. When I thought about writing this, I
considered what scars were already there, the effect they have had
and what they mean to me.

The two scars from my bike crash - one on head, the other on my
shoulder - the latter which is quite visible - but speaks of a time
when I was out cycling so much. They tell of an act of the kindness

of strangers who took care of us – took us in and made tea, gave my cycling companion a lift to get her car. Not to mention the crazy perspective I had of life where I didn't go to hospital and was working the next day at 8am with a, black eye and severe headache. It took over two years to treat the resulting concussion.

The caesarean-section scar - for so long almost hidden as it had contracted over the years with adhesions forming, hidden under the surface but causing so many gastric and gynaecological issues. I was always so proud that you couldn't see my scar, now I look down and am delighted it is visible. Happy as my tissue can move more easily around it. It gave life to my son, not the birth of choice - I was quite remote and detached from the experience - but now I feel a greater connection through it.

The almost invisible scars from my childhood: on my right knee when I fell down a hole in the Isle of Wight; on my left thigh when I cut my leg on a large nail sticking out through the carpet; above my right eye when my sister pushed me into the side of the record player - back in the day when they were a large piece of furniture - 1970's teak! They have a story to tell.

Now the breast cancer scars, one across my chest wall where my right breast used to be, the other on the edge of the left breast, another under my left armpit and finally where the portacath was placed. They tell this story

Rather than look every day and feel sad about the loss of my breast or even that I have had cancer, I observe and work to develop a relationship with them of pride and honour. I lived through this with such fortitude.

I sought treatment from my friend Liz Crosland, who is a holistic therapist and trained in ScarWork™ Therapy. Psychologically, allowing another person other than my breast surgeon to touch the scars was a powerful part of this healing process. Over time, the appearance of the scars improves as the scar tissue is less restrictive and glides more freely. My body is accepting of the scar, and the scar moves in greater coherence with the rest of my body.

In spring 2021, for the first time, I went somewhere beyond the house wearing anything less than full winter walking gear. Wearing only a t-shirt, I tried on some clothes in a store and became aware that I was self-conscious about how I looked. The headscarf or bald head and my flat, uneven chest. Over the coming weeks and months as I ventured out and tried to wear different clothes – a summer, strappy top - I learnt to adapt my style and looked for ways to still feel feminine.

I have my prosthesis, the fake silicon boob that fits inside my special bras. I do wear it on occasions if the outfit requires it, but the bra sits over my mastectomy scar and makes it itchy and sore. I am always aware of where the scar ends under my arm as the bra strap passes over it. I tend to have this urge to rearrange it. As a general rule, playing with your fake boob in public probably isn't the cleverest idea! For the most part, I feel more myself when I wear a camisole, more affectionately known as my 'nanna vest'. The right side of my chest is concave - there is only skin and ribs where the breast used to be, so it does draw your gaze to it. Most friends tell me that they don't even notice it. Most of the time, I am not concerned, but every now and again I catch myself. A passing moment of sadness that I allow myself to feel, knowing it will fade.

"I am thinking of getting a tattoo. Can you recommend someone?"

Now there are words that I never thought I'd say! I must wait a little longer for the scar to heal, but then I might have one. Originally, I thought I wanted to cover it up, to hide it. As time has passed, I see it as a badge of honour of all that I have been through, so my ideas are changing as to what this might look like. It is a test about truly being comfortable in oneself and believing more than ever that what is on the inside is enough.

Donna Ashworth Poem

I follow this poet on social media. This poem struck a chord as I had started to write the chapter on my battle scars and she said so much of what I was hoping to express. Printed with permission of Donna Ashworth.

Make Peace With Your Body

Make peace with your body today my friend,
for it has toiled for many years just to keep you alive.
It has grown, weathered virus and disease,
healed countless wounds and fought many unseen battles, to keep your soul intact for its journey through this life.

Yes it has changed but it has been changing since the day you were born.
And it will continue to change until the day you die.
Make peace with this.

Striving against this change is like trying to blow away the wind. Futile, pointless, misery-making.
Your body has served you well and done so with your daily hate and disapproval.
It has suffered years of daily, hourly negativity, pulsing its way from your brain to your cells…
Not good enough, not attractive enough, not perfect.

And every day you thought it wasn't perfect, it really, truly was.

It was keeping you alive, supporting your rash decisions, counteracting your foolish mistakes, doing everything in its power to stay in the game.
For you.

Make peace with your body today, my friend, say your apologies, right your wrongs and move on with appreciation.

You are blessed.
Look around you, not everyone is so blessed.
Not everyone is breathing, walking, thriving.

And whilst you are looking around, see that nobody is perfect. The way a body looks, says nothing about its strength, its longevity, its endurance.
This is not a rehearsal, this is your one shot at a life well-lived.
Make it count.

Donna Ashworth

Vignette: A Year On....... Unexpected Findings

Let me start by saying that these words are not the ones I anticipated writing when I planned to write about this day. My expectations of what this day would be like were not realised. The feeling I have is that I have arrived at the inflexion point in this part of my journey. The sense of calm and serenity at this moment is so powerful; like floating on your back in the lake and letting the water take you where it is going and being completely comfortable with that.

During our trip to the Lake District in April after the completion of my radiotherapy treatment, I decided I wanted to go away for the anniversary of my diagnosis. We decided to walk up Catbells in Keswick. Derwentwater is one of my favourite places. I think this comes from so many wonderful memories of holidays spent each summer at the campsite in Braithwaite, nestled in the valley surrounded by the rounded, curved slopes of Skiddaw and the Northern Fells. Now we have reached the 28th of July 2021.

In the days running up to going away I was quite melancholy and pensive, almost to the point of being anxious about how I might feel on the day. Waves of sadness, possibly grief, kept lapping at my feet. I was almost expecting a torrent of tears to arrive as we walked up the hill. On the drive up the M6 to Keswick, there was a moment when the tears pricked the back of my eyes and started to trickle down my cheeks; it was only a moment and it passed as quietly as it came. The underlying emotion was one of disbelief, that any of this has happened to me. Not sadness, though.

And yet when the day came, I barely thought about it. Neither Paul nor Liz mentioned it and they did not need to. The words were not absent. They simply were unnecessary.

We had the loveliest walk up Catbells. In between the Lakeland showers, there were moments of beautiful sunshine - lots of taking on and off waterproofs. For our lunch stop, we found a small bay at the edge of the lake and were fortunate enough to have it to ourselves. The walk up Catbells had been quite busy, as we had expected, but the people thinned out as we descended and made our way down to the lakeside for our return walk. There were only the three of us and a few courageous ducks who seemed quite interested in our picnic. The quiet and the still calm of the lake were quite stunning. We all paused to take in the silence.

A lot has happened, and everything has changed. One is that all the work I have done on myself has altered how I am, how I can be. On that walk, I was in the moment, taking one step up the path at a time and not thinking about anything other than the next step. No planning about how I was going to do this or that when I got home, or where we were going to eat that night or ...... whatever. You all know the drill. The drive to be constantly doing or thinking about what you are going to do or reviewing what you have done. The powerful part was that I was not thinking about the fact that I was just being. It simply was, and I was enjoying it as it happened. This is where I feel so appreciative of all that I have achieved, this calmness of my mind. Present in each moment, it feels like the most incredible place to be.

12

Now What?

"Can't stop the spirits when they need you
This life is more than just a read-through."

— *Anthony Kiedis, 'Can't Stop', Red Hot Chili Peppers*

Now what? I wrapped this memoir up in a lovely package from the day of my diagnosis to the same day 12 months later. So many things have happened, I've learned so much and have initiated so much change.

I emerged out of the fire and started to spread my wings and began to feel some comfort in this new form of myself.

Now what? Back to life. Back to living. Experiencing other goings-on that aren't about me having cancer. Adapting to the absence of the safety of the treatment framework. Resisting the expectations and the 'shoulds' in my life - whether real or imagined. Learning not to react but to respond to the world around me.

I find myself in a situation that, on the one hand, feels like almost everything I wanted. More time, less stress. Selling the business has removed so much worry and given me the space to recover. However, that space can sometimes feel like a void, an empty void

I don't know how to fill. I tell myself I don't need to fill it. Well, not always.

What I want to take away from these 12 months of my life is the lesson I learnt to be present in each day. My continued exploration into the yoga teachings about movement practice, our breath and meditation have brought a much-needed awareness of my body and a calmness to my mind. When I find myself looking back wistfully on those chemo days, I know I've lost track. I know I am sidestepping into the place I was when I needed to always be doing and planning.

We all live in an uncertain world. If nothing else, the COVID pandemic must have taught us that. How to get comfortable with uncertainty is the lesson I wish to keep mastering. Most of the time, I think I can handle the uncertainty of whether the cancer will return. I cannot live my day-to-day life worrying about it. would drive myself insane. The fear is there, and I acknowledge it when it arises. I remember how to accept a situation I cannot change and work out what actions, if any, I am able to take. To do otherwise is to store up further trauma in my body. I talk about the fact that I want to live for every day, not quite as if it were my last, but not to postpone too many things for 'later'. Loving my family, relishing the fantastic opportunities I am fortunate to have, laughing and living, crying and playing.

I use my routine and the structure of my day to keep me on the path. I give myself permission to feel and allow myself space to not always know. Somewhere along the way, we need to have fun. Life isn't a read-through. We only get one shot at it so take pleasure in the smallest of things to make each day feel like it was worth it.

Someone said to me that having cancer has acted like a catalyst for change but that I haven't changed. I'm not a different person - I unveiled who I am. Being in a situation where we take a long, hard look at ourselves, our lives and how we interact with those around us, we often discover everything we need is already within us. We are our own greatest asset. Over the past few years, my body has been keeping the score and telling me that change was needed, but I was too distracted to truly listen. As I learn to be, to find stillness and calm, it is quiet enough to hear. I create the space to be myself.

With Gratitude

I thank you with all my heart for taking the time from your life to share my words. I leave you with a quote from Mary Oliver that rings truer now than ever.

"Tell me, what is it you plan to do with your one wild and precious life?"

— *Mary Oliver, The Summer Day*

Acknowledgements

Writing this book has become a journey in itself. As I travelled the path of my diagnosis and treatment, I also travelled the path of learning how to write. It was challenging to embark on something completely out of my comfort zone. Whilst I felt vulnerable to put myself out there as a writer, through it I discovered the sheer pleasure of expression.

From that initial spark to embark on this endeavour to the flames that created all these words on the page, I have had so much loving and generous support.

Firstly, to Georgia Varjas for inspiring me to start and guiding me through the early days in her Women's Writing Circle. This gave me the belief that I had a story worth telling. My thanks to another member of the circle, Anne-Josee Laquerre, for her friendship and encouragement, as we found our way as first-time writers.

My enduring thanks goes to the wonderful Brita Fernandez Schmidt - both for writing the Foreword and also as my inspiration, friend and mentor. Uplifting me whenever we communicate and consistently reminding me how trusting myself releases my power.

There have been a number of people who have coached and supported me - whether in a formal relationship or through their friendship. I hasten to make a list for fear that I miss anyone out, but the following people shared their particular pearls of wisdom when I needed to hear them. Dr Sam Collins, thank you for being the catalyst and facilitator who brings women together to believe in their collective strength and for giving me the belief that I can be whatever I want to be. My deepest gratitude goes out to Randy Masingale, for helping me see the extraordinary and making sense of the transition through the various incarnations of 'Jacqui'! To Diane Lee, Chris Murphy, Simon Hartley and Chris Cook, I am forever grateful for those timely conversations that struck a chord and brought such clarity.

Committing the words to paper is only part of the story, and this book would not exist without the help of my editor, Michelle Emerson - thank you for your patience as I negotiated the process and learnt from my mistakes - and my graphic designer, Louise Carrier for her endless enthusiasm and positivity. My thanks to Donna Ashworth for permitting me to share her wonderful poem that encapsulated living with our bodies exactly how they are. And to Cecilia Costello for providing the environment where I could record my journey through her beautiful images. It was a vulnerable experience but so worthwhile.

In this story, I shared so much about all the places I go to create the space for my body, mind and spirit. I must thank Dawn Waldron for changing my relationship with my nutrition and alcohol. Elaine Frazer for opening the window of opportunity to quieten my mind. Jennifer-Lynn Crawford, Sharon Cummins and Liz Crosland for all the hands-on therapy - I so love to be the patient. To a special young woman, Ella Young, for offering yoga to me in those early days in such a way that my delicate body and mind could receive it and for continuing to inspire me to practise and be present. To my fellow yoga teachers, Emma Molly, Mary Byrne-Halaszi and Michelle Sowden, as we walk the path of incorporating these ancient teachings into our lives.

I am blessed with the most beautiful friends who make my world a better place. Alison Spencer, Claire Hartley, Liz Crosland, Susan Divers, Prue Kiddie, Debra Allen, Jen Cardew, Nell Mead, Dorren Killens, Emma Roberts, Laura O'Shaughnessy, Alyssa Twist Light, - you have travelled alongside me over the years - some decades, other less so - but you were all present in this portion of my life. No words can truly express what that means to me.

To my fellow sisters who have braved their own breast cancer journey, you are my inspiration and soul mates. In particular, thank you to Claire Turner and Siobhán Freeney, who offered me a seat at their table when I did not know which way to turn and for the work they do to advocate for Lobular Breast Cancer and further the research into the disease.

And, of course, to Paul and our children, Nathaniel and Robin. It certainly hasn't been easy but we keep striving to be better and to love each other. To be there for each other, however that looks now. Thank you for being your unique, extraordinary selves, you mean the world to me. And finally to my dog Jess - forever my companion.

About the Author

Inspired by her experience, Jacqui now runs a coaching business to work with others to develop their own individualised approach to creating space in their lives to prioritise their health and well-being. She is passionate about others making choices in their lives.

Her background was originally in corporate sales after achieving a Masters degree in Engineering. After 7 years, she made the bold decision to return to university to qualify as a physiotherapist, wanting a role that made an impact on the lives of others. She went on to build her own private practice which she ran for 13 years. She sold the business in 2021 after completing her cancer treatment. More recently she completed her Yoga Teacher Training and offers services both locally and online to share the peace and joy she has uncovered in her own practice.

Jacqui lives in Yorkshire, in the North of England, with her husband Paul, their children, Nathaniel and Robin, and their dog, Jess.

This is her first book and is a personal reflection of her experience of a breast cancer diagnosis and treatment. It is by no way offering any medical advice.

More information about Jacqui's services can be found at:

https://jacquitaylor.net

Instagram: @jacquisonelife

Facebook:facebook.com/jacqui.taylor.jacquisonelife

LinkedIn: www.linkedin.com/in/jacqui-taylor-jacquisonelife

Twitter: @jacquislife

Bibliography

Marc Brackett, Ph.D., *Permission to Feel: Unlocking the Power of Emotions to Help our Kids, Ourselves and our Society Thrive* (Celadon Books, 2019)

Brené Brown, *Braving the Wilderness. The quest for true belonging and the courage to stand alone* (Vermilion, Penguin Random House, 2017)

Brita Fernandez Schmidt, *Fears to Fierce - A Woman's Guide to owning her Power* (Rider, Penguin Random House, 2021)

Rick Hanson, Ph.D. with Richard Mendius, MD, *Buddha's Brain: The practical neuroscience of happiness, love & wisdom* (New Harbinger Publications, Inc., 2009)

Bessel Van der Kolk, *The Body Keeps the Score: Mind, Brain and Body in the Transformation of Trauma* (Penguin Random House, 2014)

Kelly DiNardo & Amy Peace-Hayden, *Living the Sutras: A Guide to Yoga Wisdom Beyond the Mat* (Shambhala, 2018)

Eckhart Tolle, *The Power of Now: A Guide to Spiritual Enlightenment* (Yellow Kite, 2020)

Other Resources

Aspire, Dr Sam Collins - https://www.aspireforequality.co.uk/

Lobular Breast Cancer UK - https://lobularbreastcancer.org.uk/

Dawn Waldron, Nutritional Therapist and Nutrigenetic Counsellor- https://dawnwaldron.com/

LifeCode Gx https://www.lifecodegx.com/

Yes to Life: The UK's integrative cancer care charity https://yestolife.org.uk/

ScarWork™ https://scarwork.uk/

Printed in Great Britain
by Amazon

16877114R00092